11-21-63

# EUROPEAN FOLKLORE
## Council of Europe

# I

# EUROPEAN FOLKLORE SERIES

A COLLECTION
PUBLISHED UNDER THE AUSPICES OF THE COUNCIL
FOR CULTURAL CO-OPERATION
OF THE
COUNCIL OF EUROPE

VOLUME N° 1

## EUROPEAN FOLK TALES

ROSENKILDE AND BAGGER
COPENHAGEN
FOLKLORE ASSOCIATES
HATBORO, PENNSYLVANIA
1963

# EUROPEAN FOLK TALES

Edited by

**LAURITS BØDKER**
**CHRISTINA HOLE, G. D'ARONCO**

**ROSENKILDE AND BAGGER**
COPENHAGEN
**FOLKLORE ASSOCIATES**
HATBORO, PENNSYLVANIA
1963

The fly-leaf illustration is from the first atlas of the world
by Abraham Ortelius, about 1570

## CONTENTS

# PREFACE

The Committee of Ministers of the Council of Europe decided in 1957 to sponsor the publication of a collection of works on European folklore, each dealing with a given genre.[1] The first volume, devoted to European Folktales, was entrusted to fil. lic. Laurits Bødker, director of the Nordisk Institut for Folkedigtning, in collaboration with Miss Christina Hole, editor of *Folklore,* Oxford, and Professor Gianfranco D'Aronco, Direttore del Seminario di Filologia Moderna presso la Facolta di Lettere e Filosofia, University of Padua (Italy).

After a preliminary discussion the editors agreed to distribute the work between themselves as follows: Professor D'Aronco undertook to collect material from the Latin countries, while Mr. Bødker was to provide texts from the rest of Europe, to write the introduction and the necessary notes, and to prepare the manuscript for the press. The stylistic revisal of the texts before going to press was entrusted to Miss Hole, who also provided the material from England.

It was agreed that the selection of texts should be made with adult readers in mind, and that as far as possible such texts only were to be brought together as were hitherto unprinted, or at any rate only printed in more or less inaccessible publications. As a guide to which types of folktale should be included and to their distribution by countries, a preliminary type-list was drawn up early in 1959 by Mr. Bødker and circulated to a number of European folklorists, who were asked to recommend the types that would best represent their countries. These proposals were then discussed at a conference held during the International Congress for Folktale Research in Kiel and Copenhagen, in August 1959, where it was agreed that the selection should be made mainly from member countries of the Council of Europe or countries having acceded to the European Cultural Convention.[2]

1. The decision of the Committee of Ministers was taken on the advice of a working party of folklore specialists which met in Strasbourg in June 1957 under the chairmanship of Mr. Kuypers, head of the Belgian delegation and present Chairman of the Council for Cultural Co-operation, which initiated the scheme in the Committee of Cultural Experts.
2. These are (at the end of 1962): Austria, Belgium, Cyprus, Denmark, France, Germany, Greece, the Holy See, Iceland, Ireland, Italy, Luxembourg, the Netherlands, Norway, Spain, Sweden, Switzerland, Turkey, and the United Kingdom.

The several texts were accordingly selected by folklorists in the countries represented, who have likewise supervised the translation of the texts into English. This somewhat complicated procedure has to some extent delayed the publication; on the other hand, it has ensured that the selection of the text has been in the most competent hands. For the interest and generous co-operation given them the editors wish to express their thanks to Brynjulf Alver (Oslo), Jouko Hautala (Helsinki), Gottfried Henssen (Marburg), Joseph Hess (Luxembourg), Waldemar Liungman (Djursholm), John Mc-Innes (Edinburgh), Séamus O'Duilearga (Dublin), Roger Pinon (Liège), Warren E. Roberts (Bloomington), J. R. W. Sinninghe (Breda), Georg Spyridakis (Athens), Einar Ol. Sveinsson (Reykjavík), Ahmet Kudsi Tecer (Istanbul), Marie-Louise R. Tenèze (Paris) and Carl-Herman Tillhagen (Stockholm).

Size and typography have been decided in consultation with Professor E. Seemann, Professor L. Schmidt, and Professor Dag Strömbäck who are the editors of the next volumes in the series.[3] Mr. H. C. Huus (Copenhagen) has rendered valuable aid in preparing the introduction and has revised the proofs of the whole text. Further, the editors are especially grateful to Mr. B. Holbek (Copenhagen) who has put in a great deal of work on the practical preparation of the texts.

Grateful acknowledgement is also made to the Council for Cultural Co-operation of the Council of Europe for sponsoring the series and to the Secretariat of the Council of Europe whose representative Mr. Victor de Pange, head of the Cultural Affairs Division, has given constant and active support without which this collection would scarcely have seen the light of day.

---

3. Vol. No. 2 will be devoted to European ballads, and published under the editorship of Professor Strömbäck (Director, Dialect and Folklore Institute, Uppsala) and Professor Seemann (Director of the Deutsches Volksliedarchiv, Freiburg).

   Vol. No. 3 will be devoted to Theatre, and published under the editorship of Professor Schmidt (Director, Österreichisches Museum für Volkskunde, Wien).

# INTRODUCTION

The European folktales are a special form of prose fiction living in oral tradition, and whose form, growth, and diffusion are dependent on the individual narrator and his audience. As a special literary genre it has been known in Europe for at least 2500 years. The oldest evidence known consists of the hints, fragments, or entire texts which have been shaped and adapted by the Greek writers of antiquity to conform with current literary standards, to be inserted as narrative elements in myths, epics, dramas, and historical works. This adaptation means that it is often difficult to see which tales have been used, and what really was their form and content before they got into the hands of the poets. The only thing known with certainty is that they are older than the poets who have used them, and that they have been living both before and after, independent of the written word, which was of slight importance so long as the art of reading was confined to the few.

The tales are found in various forms, the most important of which, the folktale proper, is about noble princes or poor herdsmen who win the princess and half the kingdom by heroic fights with supernatural antagonists such as dragons or giants, about marriages between men and supernatural beings, about speaking and helpful animals, about good fairies and wicked men, who all inhabit a world which is indeed supernatural but at the same time so closely related to the world of man that the actors can go from one sphere to the other without ceremony, and without causing any real wonderment. Part of these folktales can also have more realistic traits, in that the hero may achieve his aim by cunning and stratagems; and closely related to this group are the many jokes and anecdotes which often have a very earthy and realistic gibe at silly people and haughty persons of rank. As a special group the so-called fables are usually considered, short narratives about men and more especially about animals, a genre developed into a fine art by writers such as the legendary slave Aesop, Hesiod, Archilochus, Aeschylus, Sophocles, Plato, Aristotle, etc. without, however, losing every connection with popular tradition.

All these forms are mentioned and used in old literature, for example by Aristophanes, who in the *Wasps,* staged in 422 B.C. (ab. 2385 years ago) lets Bdelycleon say that he will not listen to tales about Lamia (a witch) and Cardopion (a pigmy smith), or about the cat and the mouse, all of which must have been known to his audience, since it is sufficient for him to hint at the titles – he will listen only to stories about real men. By that time there was already in Greece a "classic" literature, represented among others by Homer, whose famous works are teeming with motifs and elements which are found also in more recent European folktales and which in some cases can be traced back to the older civilizations around the Eastern Mediterranean. This means that even in those distant ages there have existed tales which in spite of boundaries, wars, and the language barriers have easily migrated from one country to another in a perpetually oozing, almost subterranean cultural stream, conveyed exclusively by the personal contact between men who take an interest in listening to a good story and passing it on to others.[1]

Thus, in the *Iliad,* we hear about the fratricide Bellerophon, the son of Glaucus and grandson of Sisyphus, who must flee to Proetus, the King of Tiryns, whose wife, Anteia or Stheneboea, gets enamoured of Bellerophon, and, when her advances are spurned, accuses him of having tried to seduce her, thereby enraging Proetus, who dare not, however, kill him for fear of the furies, and therefore invents a stratagem, sending Bellerophon to Anteia's father, Iobates, the King of Lycia, with a letter urging him to kill his daughter's ravisher. King Iobates, however, loth to kill a guest, tries to destroy him in some other way by setting him a number of dangerous tasks, the first of which is that of killing the Chimaera, a firebreathing female monster with a lion's head, a goat's trunk, and a serpent's tail. Bellerophon gets hold of the winged horse Pegasus and defeats the Chimaera by riding over her, shooting arrows at her, and thrusting between her jaws a spearhead with a lump of lead, which when molten by her breath, oozes down her throat, and destroys her bowels.

The monster-killer as hero is a very common trait in European folk-tales, and is found at several places in the present collection (pp. 93, 142ff., 175, etc.). It is also found in a number af national hero-tales. About Hadding, one of the kings in early Danish tradition, it is told by Saxo Grammaticus (about A. D. 1200) that one day he learned, that Regnild, the Norwegian king's daughter, was promised to a jotun. Indignant that so sad a fate should be hers, he went to Norway and killed the jotun after a very hard fight, in which he received many a wound. Regnild cured her deliverer without knowing who he was, and in order that later she might recognize him she marked his leg by putting a golden

---

1. A comprehensive survey of this material is available in *Robert Graves:* The Greek Myth. 1955 (Penguin Books).

ring into one of his wounds. Later on, permitted by her father to make her own choice, she invites all the suitors to a feast, and touching them carefully for the mark she had put herself she arrives at King Hadding to find that he is her rescuer, and marries him in return for his deed. This is one of the oldest Nordic versions of the tale of the dragon-slayer with the usual identification, in the folktales most often by means of a ring in the hair, or, as in the Finnish tale about "The Princess and the Peasant" (p. 17), by means of a mark on the forehead. The same story is told in the Old Irish Cuchulain Cycle. Another famous hero is Beowulf, the son of Ecgtheow, who slays the monster Grendel, which every night comes up from the moors and mist-ridden fens to Heorot, King Hrothgar's celebrated hall, to kill the sleeping warriors. Beowulf, who is later killed by a dragon, is epically akin to the Nordic Sigurðr and the Germanic Siegfried, further to Peredur, the son of Evrawc, who according to the Welsh *Mabinogion* (11the century) kills the serpent Addano, and who every day fights 300 knights and slays them; their horses, however, carry their dead bodies back to their castle, where the women, like the witch in the Irish folktale (p. 146), resuscitates them, that the fight may be resumed next day.

Another monster-killer is the hero Perseus, whose life-story is one long folktale. He is the son of Zeus, who descended to his mother as a golden rain, and he begins his heroic life by killing the Gorgon Medusa after receiving magic objects from the Stygian Nymphs, who have one eye and one tooth in common. Later he flies to Egypt by means of the magic sandals, and from there to the coast of Philistia, where he sees a naked woman chained to a sea-cliff. This woman is Andromeda, who like the heroine of the Austrian folktale (p. 92) is to be given to a monster. He kills the monster, and in reward is married to Andromeda.

The false accusation by a woman, as in the tale of Bellerophon and Anteia, is a very common motif in the European folktales, and dates very far back, being told already about Joseph and Potiphar's wife, and likewise found in one of the oldest folktales of the world, the story of Batu and Anup, recorded on an Egyptian papyrus which is about 3200 years old. The fatal letter given to the hero for delivery is likewise found in the Old Testament, where David uses the same method to rid himself of Urias. A third Biblical motif, that of Moses and Pharaoh's daughter, is also found in the folktales (p. 191) and in Greek myths for example about Cycnus, the son of Poseidon, who was born in concealment and exposed on the seashore, and found there by some fishermen seeing a swan coming down to comfort him. Cycnus is later married to Phylonome, who gets enamoured of her own stepson, Tenes. The same fate overtakes Peleus, who on account of murder must fly to King Acastus. Cretheis, the king's wife, makes vain efforts to seduce him, and after her failure accuses him before her husband, who, loth to kill a guest, challenges him to a hunting contest on Mount Pelion. Peleus wins because he has been given a magic sword by the gods, which has the virtue of making its owner victorious in hunting and in war. Acastus' followers, however, asserting that it is he who killed the many stags, bears, and boars, scoff at Peleus for his incompetence, to which Peleus, showing them the tongues of the animals, which he has cut off in advance, replies that the dead themselves shall decide the case. Here, then, Peleus uses the same method as that of the hero in the Austrian folktale (p. 93), who likewise wins the princess by killing the dragon with a special sword and showing the tongues to prove his deed. Later on Peleus is married to the Nereid Thetis, a mythical parallel to Cluasach's marriage to the Sea-Woman (p. 135). Peleus wins Thetis by a fight with her in a cave where she is in the habit of having her midday sleep. During the fight Thetis changes into fire, water, lion, serpent, and at last into a slippery cuttle-fish squirting ink at him, a series of transformations which, in a somewhat different form, is also found in the Scottish folktale (pp. 130f.). In the latter tale the hero transforms himself into a stallion pony, which is sold by his father to the King of the Black Art, at feature reminding of the above-mentioned Egyptian story, where Batu changes into a bull, which is given to Pharao by Anup.

In the *Odyssey* it is told that after the conquest of Troy Odysseus has to roam for ten years before returning home to his wife in Ithaca. On his long voyage he has a lot of strange experiences: he visits Circe, who gives drugged food to the hungry sailors and beats them on the shoulders with a stick thus changing them into pigs (cf. pp. 94ff.); he arrives at Hades, like the heroine in the Irish folktale (p. 136), sails past the Siren Island, between the monsters Scylla and Charybdis, and through the Symplegades, rocks which, like the mountain in the Greek folktale (p. 193), will open and shut by themselves. His best known experience, however, which is still told as a folktale or legend, is his visit to Polyphemus, the son of Poseidon, a great sheep-farmer, yet preferring human flesh; at each meal he devours two sailors, until Odysseus succeeds in having him blinded by means of a glowing wooden stick; then escaping under the bellies of the sheep he sails away from the shouting cyclop, who tells all and everybody who cares to listen that "Nobody" has blinded him.

All these stories and many others are typical instances of the sailors' yarns which have been told from time immemorial by sailors in the

Mediterranean and are still to be heard all over the world. They have much resemblance to Sindbad's stories in the *Arabian Nights,* where among other points of resemblance we also meet the bird Rok corresponding to the bird Griffin in the Irish folktale (p. 151). The oldest known instance of this genre seems to be a story found in an Egyptian papyrus dating from a time before the 19th century B.C.

Another sailor's end which the poets have elevated into the heroic-mythical sphere, is the story about Jason and his cruise with the good ship Argus to Colchis for the Golden Fleece, which is guarded day and night by an unsleeping dragon, a far-famed cruise known already to the Homeric Age, when a ballad-cycle about Argus' voyage to the land of Aeëtes was on everybody's lips. The crew consists of a number of heroes with many marvellous faculties, among them Heracles, the strongest man who ever lived, the sharp-eyed Lynceus, the oracle-interpreter Mopsus, the master musician Orpheus, the champion Polydeuces, the winged Boreads Calais and Zetes, who win every race, Periclymenus, who can change himself into any shape, etc., i. e. a crew very reminiscent of the extraordinary companions who help the Head-Falconer in the Turkish folktale (p. 209), and of Strong Peter in the Lappish tale (p. 43). On their way to Colchis, the Argonauts, as they were called, go through the Symplegades and past the Land of the Amazons, before Jason arrives at Colchis, where, thanks to Eros, Medea, the daugher of Aeëtes, gets enamoured of Jason and helps him with the difficult tasks which he is to perform in order to obtain the Golden Fleece – to plough the fields of Ares with two fire-breathing bulls, and to sow the field with dragons' teeth. Later on she drugs the dragon by dropping soporific drops on its eyelids, in order that Jason may steal the Golden Fleece, after which both of them fly on the Argus with Aeëtes' ships in hot pursuit. In order to stop the pursuers Medea kills her half-brother Apsyrtus, cuts him into small pieces and throws them behind the ship, making Aeëtes stop to gather the fractions of his body in order to bury them at Tomi.

The difficult tasks to be performed by Jason bear much resemblance to the tales of Heracles and his twelve labours, and have also parallels in medieval hero-tales, for example in the *Mabinogion,* where Kilhwych is said to be enamoured of Olwen, whom he could win only by yoking a yellow and a brindled bull, clearing a hill of thorn and bushes to be burnt for manuring the field, and sowing and harvesting on the same day. In the folktales this motif is often, as in the myth about Jason and Medea, connected with flight, during which, as in the Danish tales (p. 71), the heroine changes herself and the hero into various objects. She, or an animal helper, can also, as is the case in the Finnish tale about Pigskin (p. 11), throw, or make the hero throw, various objects which are changed into insurmountable obstacles. In Denmark Saxo Grammaticus has attached the story to the great Swedish warrier Arngrim, who in order to win King Frotho's daughter must vanquish King Egder of Bjarmland and King Thengil of the Finmark, two countries which had not so far become Danish dependencies. Arngrim indeed succeeds in defeating the Finns, who, however, in their flight avail themselves of the well-known Finnish witchcraft, dropping three pebbles, which apparently are transformed into mountains that stop the pursuers. The next day the fight is resumed, and then the Finns escape by throwing snow on the ground to make it appear like a vast stream. The third day, being in lack of any magic means of rescue, they have to submit. Thereafter Arngrim vanquishes Bjarmland too, returns to Denmark, and, loaded with honours, is married to Frotho's daughter.

As the flight motif in the story about Jason and Medea is connected with other European folk literature, the latter is connected by parallels with other stories about the Argonauts, for instance about Orpheus, who is later married to Euridice. When one day she treads on a serpent and dies of its bite, Orpheus tries to bring her back to the world of men and descends into Tartarus, where by his music he charms Charon the ferryman and further the dog Cerberus, and the three Judges of Death. He then prevails upon Hades to let her go back to the Earth on condition that during the ascent he must not look back until Euridice is brought safely back to the light of day. But when he has come into the light himself, he looks around him, and she must return to the World of the Shadows. Orpheus' descent to the Realm of the Dead and his failure to observe the prohibition are common motifs in European folktales. The descent to the Realm of the Dead, for instance, has a parallel in the Irish tale "The Woman Who Went to Hell" (p. 136), and the broken ban is met as a motif in several tales, for example in "Blue-Beard" (p. 158), "King Wivern" (p. 64), "The Gwraig and the Three Blows" (p. 120), and "The Merchant and His Three Daughters" (p. 173).

Another story which bears some resemblance to the Greek one and has connection with the flight motif, is told in *Nihongi*, the first official Japanese national history (ab. 720 B.C.), in which Isanagi goes to the Realm of the Dead in order to fetch his dead sister Isanasi, who cannot, however, be saved because she has already tasted the food of the dead, and Isanagi must return alone to the earth, pursued by furies, who are stopped by head ornaments changed into vines, and a comb that is transformed into bamboo scrubs. In India a similar flight is known from the folktales as well as from literature, for example in the *Kathâsaritsâgara* (11th cent.); and in the old Egyptian tale about Batu and Anup it is told that Batu had to flee before his brother Anup after the latter's wife had accused him of an intention to violate her virtue. On his flight he is assisted by the god Re who creates a mighty stream filled with crocodiles to sever Batu from the angry Anup. A parallel to this motif in a different religious context is found in the *Exodus,* ch. 14, where the children of Israel during their flight from Egypt "walked on dry land in the midst of the sea, and the waters were a wall unto them on their right hand and on their left", whereupon the sea behind them returned to its old bed and drowned the Egyptians.

In the Old Testament several other motifs and stories are told, which reappear in more recent tales, for instance it is told in the *Judges,* ch. 11, that Jephthah "vowed a vow unto the Lord, and said, If thou shalt without fail deliver the children of Ammon into mine hands, then it shall be, that whatsoever cometh forth of the doors of my house to meet me, when I return in peace from the children of Ammon, shall surely be the Lord's"; Jephthah was victorious and returned home, and the first thing that met him was his only daughter. The same motif is found in the Greek story about King Idomeneus, who during a voyage to Crete encounters a terrible storm and in his distress promises to dedicate to Poseidon the first person he meets, who turns out to be his daughter; and it is found again as a common introductory motif in a number of modern tales, for example in the type represented in this collection by "The Merchant and His Three Daughters" (p. 173).

The close connection between the Greek myths and European tales which is here suggested by a few examples, appears mainly as similarities in the individual motifs. We cannot, however, from this fact draw any inference to a relationship between the complex folktale containing such elements and the Greek myths. We must confine ourselves to the statement that from time immemorial there has existed a complex of story-elements which has been susceptible of exploitation and is actually exploited in several literary genres. It is, however, also of importance that we are in a position to see that already in Greek antiquity there has existed a cultural connection with the older civilizations in the Near East. The lively connection between these areas has effected diffusion of material as well as spiritual blessings which have been absorbed and adopted functionally into the civilization of the borrower. The cultural contact has certainly been mainly of an oral nature; at any rate we have few examples of direct translation from one language into another, such as has been the case for instance with the story about King Rhampsinitus and his treasure, which was told to Herodotus by the Egyptian priests.

Many centuries later this cultural contact had a parallel in the literary and oral exchange which by the intermediary of the Turks and Moors brought Indian and Persian tales to Europe and at the same time was instrumental in bringing European traditions to the Near East and farther eastward to such an extent that in the case of a great many tales an almost global distribution is brought about. Derived from the *Arabian Nights* is certainly the Greek story about "The Old Man Who Cheated the Devil" (p. 195), a story which has also been attached to King Solomon and to celebrated European sorcerers such as Virgil and Paracelsus. Derived from Indian and Persian frame-stories are the Turkish short stories which are told by the fisherman's boy in order to make the princess speak (pp. 207f.); and the stories about Nasreddin Hodja (pp. 213ff.) have parallels in the Persian tradition. Of certain Eastern origin is also the Dutch story about "The Three Pedlars" (p. 104) which is found in the *Arabian Nights,* in old Hebrew tradition, in Hindu literature, and in Chinese Buddhistic legends. The Belgian tale about "The Old Cobbler" (p. 156) has approximately the same area of distribution; it may, however, have its origin in Europe and have come to Central Asia, India, and China via Persia.

These few examples will suffice to show that the tales, or their motifs and elements, are an old international literature of an oral nature before they appear in Greek literature and are retold by Homer, hinted at by Aristophanes and other writers, and recorded by Herodotus. In these and other writers we can also find certain suggestions of how and to whom the tales are told. Aristophanes in *Pluto* mentions a story-teller called Philepsius, who is said to be able to live by telling tales; four or five hundred years later Plutarch tells that during the Athenian Oschophoria festival tales of various kinds were told, and Dio Chrysostomus (born ab. 40 A.D.) gives a descripion of the life in the hippodrome of Rome, where one was playing the flute, another dancing, and yet others were displaying curious objects, or reciting poems, or singing, and one was telling a tale or a myth. Plato is the first to mention nursery tales, and demands that they must be selected with care, which admonishment is repeated by Strabo, who deems tales to be good entertainment for children, if only terror stories about witches and demons are avoided. Tertullian mentions that tales were told to children by nurses in order that they might not fall asleep, and Arnobius (ab. 300 A.D.) makes a peevish remark about the girl weavers filling the pauses in tedious work and old women finding entertainment for credulous children. Still more negative is St. Paul, who scoffs at old wives' tales (Timothy 4, 7). This negative attitude, which is fairly common, is often explained by the sober Roman temper, but of course it may also be due to the general contempt of the authors for a genre which spoils the market for the real poets. At any rate there is in classical Latin poetry a great scarcity of motifs fetched from current folktales. Ovid for instance does indeed use a great many folktale elements, especially connected with various kinds of transformation, in his *Metamorphoses,* written about the beginning of our era, but mostly he only exploits such old myths as are already known, and which he adapts in a decidedly literary style. Closer to the oral tradition is Apuleius (born ab. 125 A.D.) who in his novel *The Transformations* ("The Golden Ass") makes an old woman tell the famous story about Cupid and Psyche to Lucius Apuleius:

Psyche, the most beautiful of all women, is invested with bridal ornaments in order to comply with an obscure oracle, then led up to a high mountain, whence a wind takes her down to a royal palace with invisible servants and a master who visits her every night without letting her see him, and warns her against her two sisters, whose advice will ruin her. Psyche does not follow his warning but instead one night takes the advice of her sisters to light a lamp to see who is with her in her bed. She then sees that her lover is Cupid himself, but unfortunately she happens to drop some of the burning oil on his shoulder. He awakes, hurries away in pain and lies down ill and suffering in Venus' castle. Psyche goes out into the world in search of her lost lover, and in vain asks the assistance of Ceres and Juno. At last she is advised to go to Venus, who in the meantime has got in a fury by her son's being enamoured of a mortal girl. She therefore gives Psyche a most unfavourable hearing and sets her a number of difficult tasks such as sorting out great quantities of various grains before evening, fetching wool from golden sheep, which will kill all men, fetching water from the Styx and going down to the underworld by a path filled with dangers, there to ask Proserpina for divine beauty, which Psyche is to take back to Venus in a box. But Proserpina fills the box with sleep, and when on her way back Psyche once more breaks a ban and opens the box, she falls into a death-like slumber, from which she is awakened by Cupid, who in the meantime has recovered; and Jupiter and the Council of Heaven decide that the lovers shall have each other.

This story can still be recorded as a popular tradition in Europe, only leaving out the mythological apparatus, without which writers of antiquity do not seem to have been able to tell a good story.

The theme of love which overcomes all difficulties is found in many tales in many different garbs. Thus a close parallel to the classic story is the Irish story about "The Woman Who Went to Hell" (p. 136); the Italian tale about "The Serpent Son" (p. 182) and the English story about "The Small-Tooth Dog" (p. 114) are usually referred to the same type. The Italian tale has an introduction very reminiscent of the Danish tale about "King Wivern" (p. 64), whereas the sufferings of the heroine in the rest of the story, like Máire's visit to Hell in the Irish story, are typical traditional embodiments of the classic motif. On her way to the underworld Psyche meets a lame ass which she must not help, Charon the ferry-man, whom she is to give a coin, a fleeting corpse of an old man whom she must not pity, three women whose clothes she must not touch, and the dog Cerberus to which she is to give one of her sops. This number of bans and warnings have parallels in the folktales, among others in the Italian story of "The Black and the White Bride" (p. 176).

In the course of the following centuries, however, a quite new genre springs up, the so-called Christian legends, which seem in their oldest forms to be fairly credible accounts of the lives and doings of martyrs and confessors, seen in a religious and edifying light. But gradually as these stories become ever more popular, they are coloured by the oral tradition and become a sort of religious tales, in which the apostles, saints, virgins, and other good men and women wage a glorious and successful war against the Devil and all his crowd, who like the dragons and monsters of the folktale seem to have devoted their life exclusively to doing harm and to destroy the world of man and the foundation of life, which is the Christian faith. In this warfare the good hero or heroine is always assisted and supported by supernatural and divine beings, such as angels, apostles, and saints, and even the Virgin Mary acts as helper (p. 186), as helper and godmother (p. 160), and as the refuge and deliverer of sinners (p. 204). These actors seem to have taken over the function which is usually performed among others by old women, the helpful dead, good maids, and speaking animals. A rich lore of this kind is still abundant in the Catholic countries, as an independent literary genre as well as interwoven in popular tradition. In the Protestant countries of Northern and Western Europe these legends were officially suppressed after the Reformation, but there are still traces of them in popular tradition, in the form of pure Catholic legends which, as is the case with one of the English tales, can be attached to a medieval hero such as King Arthur

(p. 116), as well as in the form of tales of a more humoristic nature about Our Lord and St. Peter (p. 112).

Beside the Christian legends another religious genre is developed gradually, namely the *exempla,* a classic fable or more popular anecdote the content of which can form the basis of a sermon. But in the rich store of literary and popular tradition found in the collections of exempla there are also real tales, for example the oldest European variants of the Dutch stories about "The Three Pedlars" (p. 104) and about Our Lord as matchmaker (p. 112). The oldest known exempla are found in the homilies *In Evangelia* of St. Gregory I (before 604 A.D.) but it was not until the 13th and 14th centuries that popular preachers, such as the Dominicans and the Franciscans, who were fond of listening to a good story and telling one themselves, developed the exempla into a narrative art which would collect listeners everywhere: in streets and market-places, at fairs and cross-roads, in the precincts of churches and inside them, at inns and places of pilgrimage. Perhaps without knowing it themselves, these migrant preachers became strong competitors to the migrant artists of a more secular nature, who under various names such as jugglers, trouvères, minstrels, etc. in the Middle Ages wandered all over Europe and like their predecessors, the Roman mimes, sang, recited, and told hero tales, anecdotes, and folktales in a perpetual stream and so were instrumental in making the traditions an international oral literature, in which among other things we find the *Unibos,* the oldest European variant of "Master Sly" (p. 99).

The folktales which were thus spread from one country to another settle in the local tradition and are then told in all ranks, to adults as well as to children. As a rule the contemporary authors give only faint glimpses of this narrative tradition without giving any detailed account of what is told. This applies for example to the French poets Jehan le Chapelain (13th cent.) who in a fabliau mentions that it is customary in an inn to tell the host a story or to sing him a song, and Guibert de Nogent (ab. 1100), who in a treatise about the proper manner of conversation writes that he has learnt that some people like to embellish their conversation with simple tales and accounts of the deeds of the ancestors. About Count Balduin of Guines it is told that during the siege of Calais (1346–47) he esteemed the old people who lived with him and told about the deeds of the ancestors as well as fables and tales without any embellishment or moralizing endings. Martin Luther in a passage says that he would not for gold be without the wonderful stories he had heard both in childhood and later in life; and in *Gargantua* (1535) Rabelais makes

old Grandgousier sit down by the fireside after supper to tell his wife
and family the good old tales. Only in very few cases do the early sources
contain any information about the repertory of the times, but sometimes
suggestions are found, for example in Odd Snorrason, the monk who
about 1200 wrote a saga about King Olafr Tryggvason, and in the introduction as a sort of "blurb" asserts that it is better to listen to his story
than to those tales that are told about stepmothers, and about which
nobody knows what is true, that is to say, tales with an introduction such
as in "Marion and Jeanne" (p. 160) and "The Black Bride and the White
Bride" (p. 176).

More information is found in Noel du Fail, who in 1547 gives an
account not only of what is told but also of how it is told by Robin the
farmer at home, when in the evening he collects the working family and
servants around the fireplace, and "apres avoir imposé silence, commen-
çoit le conte de la cicogne, du temps que les bestes parloient, ou comme
le renard desroboit le poisson aux poissonniers; comme il feit battre le loup
aux lavandieres, lorsqu'il l'apprenoit à pescher; comme le chien et le chat
alloient bien loing; du lyon, roy des bestes, qui fist l'asne son lieutenant
et voulut estre roy du tout; de la corneille, qui en chantant perdit son
frommage; de Melusine; du loup garou, du Cuir d'asnette, du moyne
bourré; des fées, et que souventes fois parloit à elles familierement, mesme
la vespree passant par le chemin creux, et qu'il les voyoit dancer au bransle
pres la fontaine du cormier".

I have taken the liberty of quoting this fine description in its original
form; it would lose too much by being translated into Modern English.
The same applies to the anonymous pamphlet "The Complaynt of Scot-
lande" from about 1549, in which is given a list of tales and songs heard
among Scotch shepherds, comprising "The taylis of Cantirberrye, Robert
le dyabil duc of Normandie, The tayl of the volfe of the varldis end, Ferrand
erl of Flandris that mareit the deuyl, The taiyl of the reyde eyttyn vitht the
thre heydis, The tail quhou Perseus sauit Andromeda fra the cruel monstir,
The prophysie of Merlyne, The tayl of the giantis that eit quyk men, On fut
by Fortht as i culd found, Vallace, The bruce, Ypomedon, The tail of the thre
futtit dog of Norrouay, The tayl quhou Hercules sleu the serpent hidra that
hed vij heydis, The tail quhou the kyng of Est mure land mareit the kyngis
dochtir of Vest mure land, Skail Gillenderson the kyngis sone of Skellye,
The tayl of the four sonnis of Aymon, The tayl of the brig of the Mantribil,
The tail of syr Euan, Arthours knycht, Rauf Collyear, The seige of Millan,
Gauen and Gollogras, Lancelot du lac, Arthour knycht he raid on nycht
vitht gyltin spur and candil lycht, The tail of Floremond of Albanye that

sleu the dragon be the see, The tail of syr Valtir the bald Leslie, The tail of the pure tynt, Claryades and Maliades, Arthour of litil Bertangye, Robene Hude and litil Jhone, The meruellis of Mandiueil, The tayl of the yong Tamlene, and of the bald Braband, The ryng of the roy Robert, Syr Egeir and syr Gryme, Beuis of Southamtonn, The goldin targe, The paleis of honour, The tayl quhou Acteon vas transformit in ane hart, and syne slane be his auen doggis, The tayl of Pirramus and Tesbe, The tail of the amours of Leander and Hero, The tail quhou Jupiter transformit his deir loue Yo in ane cou, The tail quhou that Jason van the goldin fleice, Opheus kyng of Portingal, The tayl of the goldin appil, The tail of the thre veird systirs, The tayl quhou that Dedalus maid the laborynth to keip the monstir Minotaurus, The tail quhou kyng Midas gat tua asse luggis on his hede be cause of his auereis".[1]

The folktale reaches its highest literary perfection in the Italian *novella* where it is often found in a curious blend with stories from classical antiquity, tales from the Bible, fractions of hero tales about King Arthur, and contemporary anecdotes, such as is the case in the oldest collection of its kind, *Cento novelle antiche,* ab. 1300, where among other things stories are found which can still be taken down from oral tradition, for example in Turkey (pp. 205ff.). Giovanni Boccaccio uses the same technique of blending in *Il Decamerone* (1348–53), in which at least fifty stories are considered as derived from oral tradition, and a little later, in the collection by his Florentine compatriot Franco Sacchetti (1300–ab. 1400), we find several international jokes and anecdotes, among them the story about the King and the Farmer (p. 103), which seems to have been very popular among the writers of the age, since at the same time and a little later it was adapted by the Dutch author Jan van Hollant, used in a German *Fastnachtspiel,* and included in the English version of the famous medieval collection *Gesta Romanorum* (14th cent.).

More important for the knowledge of folk literature in that age is, however, *Le piacevoli notti,* published at Venice in 1550–55 by Giovanni Straparola, and containing 74 stories, half of which are derived from Italian popular tradition. By rights, therefore, this work must be counted among the earliest important collections of European folktales, where among other things we find the oldest known variants of "Master Truthful" (p. 201), "Dame Cat" (p. 197), and the story about the bunk fight

---

1. Quoted from J. Bolte and G. Polívka: Anmerkungen zu den Kinder- und Hausmärchen der Brüder Grimm, vol. IV (Leipzig 1930), pp. 60 and 62 Nos. 92 and 97 respectively. A considerable number of testimonies to the history of the folktale have been brought together in this book.

between the fisherman's son and the King of the Black Art (p. 122). Still closer to popular tradition and to the popular Neapolitan idiom is Giambattista Basile's "Lo cunto de li cunti" (i. e., the tale of tales), better known under the title *Il Pentamerone*. This book, published in 1634–36, contains about 50 folktales, which still occur in oral tradition in parts of Europe. Among them are several versions of Cupid and Psyche, a version of the Dutch tale about "The Wonder Child" (p. 108), a variant of the French story about "Marion and Jeanne" (p. 160), the Austrian story about Hans, Sepp, and Jörg (p. 92), the Greek tale of "Dame Cat" (p. 197), the Danish tale about "Ann Gej and Visivej" (p. 70), a special version of the Finnish tale about "Pigskin" (p. 10), the Italian version of "The Black Bride and the White Bride" (p. 176), the Dutch story about "The Three Pedlars" (p. 104), the Icelandic form of "Wake-Well and His Brothers" (p. 53), and the Italian stories about "The Three Oranges" (p. 178) and the big louse-skin (p. 184).

In Spain and France a similar interest in folk literature can be traced, though we never meet with such comprehensive collections as in Italy, but have to track down the material in novelists and playwrights such as Cervantes, Calderon, and Rabelais, who like a great many other writers of that age inserted the material, more especially jokes and anecdotes, in novels, plays, and epics. In Germany, on the other hand, Johannes Pauli with *Schimpf und Ernst* (1522) creates a real treasure of old and more recent tradition, and a little later Hans Sachs in his *Meisterlieder* reshapes a thousand anecdotes, fables, and short tales. It is not, however, until several generations later that Europe once more is given a collection of folktales to be compared with the Italian *novelle*. This took place in 1696, when Charles Perrault anonymously brought out his little book "Histoires ou Contes du temps passé", better known under the title *Contes de ma mere l'oye* taken from the heading on the front copper of the book. In this collection we meet a number of well-known characters, such as The Sleeping Beauty, Red Riding Hood, Puss in Boots, Cinderella, and Tom Thumb. Perrault found many imitators, especially among ladies, thus creating a special genre "contes des fées", or fairy tales, farther and farther removed from the folktales and resulting in the general disparagement of the genre among the writers of the age. A truer and juster valuation of the folktale as an independent genre with laws of its own is not found until Johann Gottfried Herder from 1773 on tried to arouse a public interest in the origin and development of the folktale, thus creating a fertile soil for the scholarly work on folk literature which from 1800 was started by the German Romantics, and, with the *Kinder- und Haus-*

*märchen,* brought out by the Grimm brothers (1812), aroused so great a European interest in folktales that in all countries it became fashionable to collect and edit the tales with tolerable correctness and make them subject to scholarly research.

This work has now been going on for 150 years, so far, however, without throwing full light on the origin and the paths of diffusion of the various tales. We only know that this remarkable literature is as old as civilization in Europe, and that for thousands of years it has been loved by princes and beggars, by children as well as adults, that poets, dramatists, and novelists have exploited it according to the tastes of their age, and depreciated it when it would not fit into the prevailing aesthetic theories of the period. But during the one hundred and fifty years that have passed since the work on the folktales was really taken in hand the public interest in oral tradition has suffered an unmistakable decline. The folktale as a fine art does not seem capable of surviving in modern civilization, perhaps because the latter is a little too hectic and does not leave time for the people to relax and listen in the right manner such as did the heroes in one of the Irish folktales (p. 145) of whom it is told that "they spent that night right pleasantly, a third of the night in story-telling, a third in the telling of the high deeds of the Fianna, and a third in deep sleep and slumber, the taste of honey on every bite they ate, and they ate no bite dry, and thus they were until dawn".

*L. Bødker.*

# FINLAND

## THE SOLDIER AND THE BAD MAN

There was once a soldier who served the Crown for a long time, and was finally allowed to go on account of his age. On his way back home he swore to himself and said:

"The Devil take that commander of mine for not giving me a pension book. How am I going to live now? I'm ashamed to beg, having served the Crown for so long."

This thought made the poor old soldier so sad that he wept. And he walked on. When he had gone a goodly distance, he met a man who asked:

"What are you swearing for, and why are you so downcast and sad?"

The soldier answered that he was swearing because his commander had not given him a pension book, and this made him anxious about what the future might have in store for him. Then the stranger said to him:

"Since your commander has failed you, why don't you become my handy man?"

"I'd be glad to take the job if I was able to work," said the soldier, "but I am not able."

"It won't be hard work," said the man. "You'll be able to do what I ask of you."

"What sort of work is it that's so easy to do?" asked the soldier.

"All you have to do is to keep cooking just one kettle," said the man.

"But who's going to fetch the firewood?" asked the soldier.

The other answered: "There'll always be wood at hand, the food is ready, and you can wear the clothes you've got on all the time you're with me." And he added that if the soldier would agree to become his handy man and serve the required three years, he could count on earning enough money to keep him for the rest of his life.

"Have you engaged any others to work for you?" asked the soldier.

"No," said the man, "you'll be all alone tending the kettle."

By now the soldier began to feel he could accept the offer made to him, but still he asked:

3

1

"Have you food enough, so we won't ever have to go hungry?"

"Plenty!" said the man.

"All right, I'll do it," said the soldier. "But how far do we have to go?"

"You don't have to worry about that," answered the man, "because I'll have you brought right back to this place, so you won't have any trouble travelling."

Now the soldier finally accepted the offer of the job. As soon as he gave his consent to the agreement, there was a thump, and he found himself inside a mountain where a kettle was boiling. This kettle, which was tremendously big, had a lid on it, so that no one could see what was inside. The man gave the soldier instructions how to cook, and he said to him:

"You mustn't lift the lid or look to see what is inside, if you want to keep our bargain. You've only got to be faithful and keep the fire going under the kettle."

And during the whole time, the soldier was not allowed to wash his face or cut his nails, shave his whiskers or cut his hair. (The wood never gave out during the whole time, and he never noticed who brought it in.) When three years had gone by, during which he had kept his promises, the man who had engaged him came and asked:

"Have you wanted for anything, and have you faithfully tended the kettle?"

The soldier answered: "I've not wanted for anything, and I have faithfully tended the kettle."

"Have you looked into the kettle?" asked his employer.

"I have not looked into the kettle."

Then his employer said: "I know full well you have been faithful. I'll certainly pay you your wages, but wouldn't you like to serve me for another three years?"

The soldier hesitated a little, and said he had felt lonely, being all alone for so long. His employer said:

"Stay, and I'll pay you more, so that you can get yourself a wife, and as big a family as you like. And you can have as much gold and silver as you want; and it won't grow any less on you."

So the soldier promised to stay on for three more years. The same contract was made; he must not look into the kettle, or wash his face, or cut his nails, or shave his whiskers, or cut his hair.

After he had tended the kettle for another two years, he thought to himself: "I'll have to peep into that there kettle and see what's inside." And he looked. Well, he saw that it was quite full of people, that kettle

2

was, and among them he saw the man who had failed to give him his pension book, in that same kettle. Well, that didn't cause him to ease up, rather did he cook with added energy, and he put extra wood on the fire, out of hatred for the fellow for being so mean.

When he had cooked for one more year, completing the three years, his employer came again and asked:

"Have you been faithful?"

"Surely have I been faithful," he answered, "only I looked into the kettle; but after that, I cooked even more faithfully."

"It doesn't matter if you've looked," said his employer, "as long as you kept on cooking, and did not stop out of astonishment."

Then he said: "Wouldn't you like to serve three more years? I'll raise your pay to as much as you'd ever want."

"I'd like to go away now and see the world," answered the soldier. "I've been all alone long enough."

"I have not had anybody so faithful in my service before," said the other, "and I certainly would like you to stay for three more years."

"No, I am already an old man. I haven't the strength to serve you any more."

"I see it's no use my demanding it either," responded his employer, "I must make good my promise."

Then he led the soldier through a door into another room, where there were two bins, one containing gold pieces and the other silver pieces. And he said:

"Take whichever you wish, as much as you think you can carry."

The soldier filled his pouch with gold, taking as much as he could carry, which was a goodly amount, and he stuffed his pockets as full of silver coins as he could. Then the other transported him to the spot where they had first met, and they made a compact that he must not shave his whiskers or wash his face or cut his hair or cut his nails until he had consulted the other and obtained permission to clean himself. If he broke his pledge, his money would begin to run out; otherwise, no matter how he lived, as long as he remained dirty, his money would last. The soldier gave his word that he would not clean himself until he received permission to do so. Then they parted company, and he started to walk along the road.

He stopped at the first house on the roadside meaning to buy something to eat. But because he was such a dreadful sight, with his long beard and long hair, nails like the claws of an eagle, skin black and sooty, and clothes in similar condition, all the people fled when he

3·

entered the house, thinking he was the Devil. So he left and went to another house. But there likewise, the people fled, so he was unable to speak to anybody. He began to grow very hungry, and he went into several more houses; but they ran away from him everywhere he went, so he could get no food.

Then he decided to visit an inn, where there would have to be an innkeeper on hand to help travellers on their way. When he reached the inn, everybody fled except the innkeeper, who hid in the back room. The soldier sat down at a table in the main room, took some coins from his pocket, and made clinking noises with them. The innkeeper heard the sounds from his hiding-place, and he secretly peeped from behind the door to see what was clinking.

The soldier noticed that the door was slightly ajar and that somebody was peeping from behind it, and he said:

"You need not be afraid of me. I'm human, even though I haven't kept myself clean."

Then he asked that food should be brought to him, since he was able to pay for it. The innkeeper dared not come out, but kept on peeping from behind the door. So the soldier put a handful of coins on the table and said:

"If you'll bring me food, you can have all this money for just one meal."

Well, that fetched the innkeeper out of the back room. He was frightened, but he came up and asked:

"Where do you hail from, stranger? Where are you travelling to?"

The soldier answered: "I'm an old soldier, and I have been released from military service, and I'm on my way back home."

"I've seen old soldiers before," said the innkeeper, "but they have not been so filthy as you are, stranger. And after all, they don't let you be dirty in the army."

"By no means do they let you be like this," said the soldier, "nor was I dirty while I was in the army. But I've been working for a man for six years since I left the army, and he wouldn't let me clean myself."

"Well, what a crazy fool that man must have been," said the innkeeper, "not letting you wash yourself or clean up!" And he asked: "Where was it?"

"I don't feel inclined to tell you," said the soldier.

"Don't you think you ought to wash now that you've left that man?" asked the innkeeper.

The soldier asked for something to eat, and the innkeeper brought

4

him some food. The soldier told him to take the money he had promised for the meal. The innkeeper took it, and then the soldier asked if he could be lodged in the house. But he was told:

"I've got so few rooms here that I can't put you up."

"I wouldn't take up such a terrible lot of space," said the soldier, "that I couldn't share the same room with the people of the house." And he added: "I'll pay for my keep."

"I'm willing enough," said the innkeeper, "but the rest of the household would object, and lots of travellers who drop in would complain about your hideous appearance, since you never wash yourself."

The innkeeper even had his doubts whether the soldier was really human. But he said he might be able to give him a lodging, provided that he cleaned himself.

"It won't do," said the soldier.

"Why not," asked the innkeeper, "if you're really a human being?"

"I am a real human being all right," answered the soldier, "even if I haven't kept myself clean, and that's a fact. But the reason is that the man I worked for these past six years wouldn't allow it."

"Well," said the innkeeper, "why should you obey him so?"

The soldier said that, if the innkeeper would not tell anybody, he would explain. The innkeeper promised not to tell, and the soldier said:

"The reason I obey is that he paid me as wages as much money in gold as I could carry, and he said it would never grow less, no matter how much I spend, on condition that I do not clean myself. And I think my employer was no real human being, for he took me inside a mountain, where I spent the whole time."

That is how the soldier explained the whole of the matter to the innkeeper.

"Well," said the innkeeper, "under such conditions it certainly would not pay you to clean yourself up."

"Won't you put me up in this house," asked the soldier, "in spite of everything? I'll pay you back many times over what I use."

"I'd need a special room," replied the innkeeper, "for I could not keep you in the sight of people. But, as I've just said, I haven't got any such room. Besides, I don't know whether I could keep you anyhow, unless you have some papers proving that you are not an ordinary tramp."

"No fear of that!" said the soldier. "I'm an honest old soldier, and I have my soldier's passport to prove it."

"Why don't you go back to the country you hail from, where your home is?" said the innkeeper.

"It's a long way to the country where my home is," answered the soldier, "and the reason I don't want to travel there is that I have already seen that people won't even give me anything to eat. When they see me, they run away. I'd have to go hungry before I got far, even though I do have money. But you can't eat money, and the farmers and their wives won't stay in place so that I can buy provisions from them, let alone other people. And even without this, none of my relatives is alive any more back in my home country, and all my old-time friends have disappeared by now, for I have been so long in the army. So it's all the same to me where I stay."

The inn was loaded with debt, and its keeper was a poor man, who was naturally pleased to have a guest with so much money. He asked the soldier if he would mind living in the *sauna,* the bath-house.

The soldier answered: "What's pleasure to an old man? The main thing for an oldster is to keep warm."

So they concluded the bargain, the soldier going to live in the sauna, and the innkeeper staying on in his house. The innkeeper received so much money that he was soon able to pay off all his debts, and to make his house more imposing than any manor-house in the country. Finally he became very rich. Gentlemen who had visited the inn before asked him:

"How have you made a fortune in such a short time, when earlier travellers could scarcely get anything but water from the whole house?"

To these gentlemen who so persistently asked questions, the innkeeper explained that there lived on his premises an old soldier who had so much money he never ran out of it, and that he was being paid so well that he had been able to recuperate his fortune. Through the gentlemen, the matter came to the attention of the King of that realm. That is to say, he learnt that there lived in his realm a man who always had plenty of money, no matter how much he spent. And the King was heavily in debt, too.

So he summoned the soldier, thinking he might likewise get some money out of him. The soldier did not want to go, knowing how dreadful he looked. But command followed command. The soldier became very downhearted, for how could he go, looking as he did? Should he clean himself, or what should he do? Should he change his clothes and go all the same? Then, one night, his old employer visited him and said:

6

"Go ahead and see the King, and do not be at all afraid; but you mustn't clean yourself any more than you have up to now."

"But what will the King do to me on account of my uncouth appearance?" said the soldier.

"Don't be at all afraid," answered his old employer. "He won't do anything to you. I know what business he had in mind when he summoned you. He is in debt, is the King, and he has learnt that you have plenty of money, and that the amount never diminishes. So he intends to get his debts paid off through you. Just you go to him. I'll give you all the money you need. Give the money to the King, but on condition that he gives you the hand of one of his daughters in marriage. If he won't, then don't give him a single penny. But if he agrees to give you his daughter's hand, then you can give him as much money as he needs. He has three daughters, and the two older ones won't give their consent; but what the youngest will do, I have no idea. And remember, I'll always be with you on that journey, although nobody else can see me."

Then the soldier left the inn and went to the King, and said:

"Here I am, the old soldier, whom Your Majesty has summoned."

"Yes, I have heard about you," said the King, "and that you are supposed to have so much money that nobody can be compared with you, and no matter how much you spend, the amount does not diminish. Is this true that I have heard about you?"

"Yes, Your Majesty, it is true."

The King asked: "How did you come by so much money?"

Then the old soldier told him honestly how he had come by the money after leaving military service.

"Why do you keep yourself so filthy?" asked the King.

The soldier explained that if he cleaned himself, his money would run out, and that he did not want this to happen because he had never received his pension.

Be that as it might, the King said he did not want to pry further into the matter. "But I do need money," he said, "if you are willing to help me and lend me some."

"Well, Your Majesty, that can surely be arranged, as much as you want, but not in very large sums, rather in small amounts, for I have no more on me than I can carry at a time; but only on condition that Your Majesty gives me your daughter's hand in marriage."

The King said: "I do not know whether my daughter would give her consent to that, because you look so very uncouth."

7

Nevertheless, he called his eldest daughter and asked her if she would agree to marrying this rich man, looking as he did. She was horrified and said: "Not anybody like that!"

The second daughter was asked the same question, and just like the first, she answered: "I would never marry anybody like that, even if I had to die!"

Then the third and youngest daughter was called in, and the King put the same question to her.

"I wish to obey His Majesty, my father," she said, "even though it is not exactly to my liking, for I wish to abide by his royal will."

To this the soldier responded:

"If you consent to a match of love with me, I shall not give you any other betrothal present now except one ribbon."

That ribbon was so strange that nothing like it had ever been seen before. It was his old employer who had given it to him; he had visited him during the night, and told him to present one half of it to his betrothed. So the soldier took a pair of scissors and snipped the ribbon in two, giving the King's daughter one half and putting the other half in his pocket. And he warned her not to lose her half, but to hold on to it until he came next time. Then he went away.

On his way home, he met his old employer, who said:

"Now you must shave off your whiskers, and clip off your hair, and clean yourself as well as you possibly can."

He told the soldier to buy himself the best princely garments he could find, and the best carriage and horses that were for sale in the whole kingdom, and to return to the King, but not to let it be known right away that he was the same man.

And his employer joined him as his manservant. The soldier turned out to be so handsome that nobody comparable to him had ever been seen before. He was both young and well dressed, in the finest of garments, and his carriage and horses were splendid and beautiful. He had a coachman to drive the horses, and everything sparkled with gold and silver, for he made them sparkle in the eyes of other people.

The soldier went to the King, acting the part of a different man, not as he was the first time, but as a Prince from some other kingdom. He offered himself as a son-in-law and requested the hand of a Princess. The King was agreeable, and called his eldest daughter first to show herself. She would have been willing to accept the Prince, but he said he did not care for her, and asked to see the second daughter. She was summoned for him to see, but he said:

8

"I don't like this one either, but I've heard there is also a third Princess. If I could see her, and if I could have her hand, I'll take her."

The third daughter came. The King asked if she wished to marry this Prince. The girl said:

"It it not right for me to make a match with another, since I have already plighted my troth, as Your Majesty knows full well."

"Where does he come from, this one to whom she has plighted her troth?" asked the Prince.

"I do not know whence he comes," answered the girl.

"Perchance he will not return to fulfill his pledge," said the Prince. But the girl answered:

"Surely he will. I cannot believe otherwise. He will surely keep his pledge."

"Well," asked the Prince, "did he give you any betrothal present?"

"He did not give me anything," said the girl.

"What sort of match was that, if no token was given?" said the Prince. "Surely he must have given some sort of token, as long as you made a match."

The girl answered that he had left her a token, but she was ashamed to say what it was.

Then the Prince said: "It makes no difference how poor it may be, or how worthless." And he insisted that she should bring it for him to see. She did not want to fetch it, but finally she did so, because he was so insistent. When she brought it, the Prince took the other half of the ribbon from his pocket and said:

"Aren't these cut from the same ribbon, and do they not fit together, though they have been cut apart in such a complicated way?" And he announced: "I am the same man as before, and the bargain was that whoever had the other half of the ribbon should be accepted as your suitor."

When they saw that the two ribbons had been cut from the same piece, they accepted him. And then he brought forth his betrothal presents, gold and silver in abundance and all sorts of splendid things never before seen, handing them over both to the King and to his bride. And he asked that the wedding be held as soon as possible. Great was the rejoicing in the King's palace, and especially because the ugly and uncouth man had changed into such a handsome and agreeable one. The other two daughters were very downcast because they had not had the sense to consent to his proposal the first time, and because after that, nobody else would take them.

9

While the youngest Princess was being married to the soldier in church, the elder sisters hanged themselves, because fortune had not smiled upon them. And the soldier's old employer shouted at the church door, while the wedding ceremony was going on and the two sisters were hanging themselves: "Aha! Aha! You got one, but I got two!"

The soldier made the King very rich, and he was rich himself.


## PIGSKIN

Once there was a beggar lad who went to a parsonage, and the parson said to him:

"I'll take you into my service, provided that, since I'm taking you so young, you serve me during the whole of my lifetime without pay."

The lad entered the parson's service, and he was treated like a son, except that the parson himself was very harsh, and the lad thought: "If only the parson would die, then I could get away from here!"

The parson died at last, and the lad received no pay. He just made a whip, and then he started off to walk towards the town.

As he was walking down a street, a certain man passed, riding in a coach drawn by two horses. The lad was lashing out with his whip, this way and that, and the coachman cried:

"Stop lashing out with that whip, it's frightening my horses!"

The lad answered: "What harm is there in my lashing? It's my own whip."

A short time later, the same coach approached him again, and the coachman cried out once more:

"Stop lashing out with that whip, it's scaring my horses!"

"What harm is there in my lashing?" retorted the lad, "it's my own whip."

The coach came by a third time, and now the man inside it called out: "Wouldn't you like to ride in my coach?" The lad climbed in, and the coach leapt into the air so suddenly that his hair stood on end like cords of brass. When the coach landed, the man said he was the Devil himself.

"Were you frightened?" he asked.

"I wasn't afraid in the least," answered the lad, "it was rather fun."

The Devil asked: "Would you like to become my handy man?" and he answered: "I would indeed." Then they went together to the Devil's castle, where the lad was put to feeding livestock.

One day, the Devil left home, and set him to tending the fire under a couple of pots; but he was not supposed to look into them to see what was inside. He was also told to give meat to a grey stallion and hay to a man. As soon as the Devil had gone, he looked into the smaller pot, and he saw, cooking inside, the parson in whose service he had first been. He heaped fuel on the fire and said: "Sink down lower!" That pleased the Devil, because he knew what the lad had done.

On the second day, he looked into the other pot. Gold was boiling in it. He thrust his arm into it up to the elbow, and he wiped all the gold off it in his hair. In the castle he kept a pig's skin that he had stripped off whole, with snout and ears and all that a pig has. When he was supposed to take the hay over to the man and meat over to the horse, he took meat to the man and hay to the horse. When he gave it the hay, the horse said:

"You've done it all backwards, and if the Devil comes, he'll kill you right away. But let's go away from here together."

"All right, let's go," answered the lad.

The horse said: "Go and take that sword off the wall. It's so heavy, you won't be able to budge it; but on that wall there hangs a flask. Take three drinks from it, and the sword will turn as light as a feather. Then take the bundle in which there is a stone, and take also one piece of wood and one pot of water, which you'll need. Then you'll find a star costume, a moon costume, and a sun costume hanging on that wall. Take them all with you."

The lad went inside and tried to lift the sword, but he could not. He drank from the flask and tried again to lift the sword; this time he was able to move it off the wall. He took a second drink and tried to lift the sword, and this time he was able to take it down from the wall. After a third drink, the sword was as light as a feather in his hand. And he took everything with him, just as the horse had told him.

He went into the stable and led the horse out, and they started off as fast as the horse could run. The Devil had taught that horse to run anywhere, in the air, and everywhere.

When the Devil came home, he saw right away that the horse and the lad had fled. He started off immediately in pursuit. When the horse and the lad had travelled a goodly distance, the horse said:

"Look behind, can you see anything?"

The lad looked behind and said:

"It looks back there as if some little bird were flying after us."

After a short while, the horse said again:

"Look again!"

11

The lad looked again, and he said:

"It's just as if a big sailing ship were following us."

"It's the Devil," said the horse. "Throw that piece of wood on the ground."

The boy threw the piece of wood on the ground, and at once a great forest sprang up, so dense that the Devil could not get through. He had to go back to fetch an axe, so that he could hack out a path for himself. When he had hacked out the trail, he started to take back the axe; but a fox said:

"Don't you take it back. I'll attend to it."

"I'll take it back myself," answered the Devil. And he took the axe back to his castle, after which he returned to the chase. But meanwhile, the two had travelled a goodly distance. Presently the horse said:

"Look back again!"

The lad looked back and said: "It's as if some little bird was flying behind us."

After a short time, the horse said once more: "Look again!"

The boy looked and said: "We're being followed by what appears like a great castle."

"It's the Devil," said the horse. "Now throw that stone in the bundle on the ground."

The lad threw the stone on the ground, and it turned at once into a great mountain, over which the Devil was unable to cross. He had to return home to fetch tools with which he could bore a way through the mountain, so that he could take up the chase once more. When he had bored a tunnel, and began to put his tools away in it, the fox ran up to him and said:

"I'll put your tools away."

The Devil had to take his tools back home again; and meanwhile the boy and the horse fled a goodly distance further.

After a time, the horse told the boy to look back again and see if anybody was following them. The boy turned his head and said:

"It's as if a little sparrow was flying behind us."

After a little while, the horse said: "Look again!"

The lad said: "It's as if a great church were coming behind us."

"It's the Devil," said the horse. "Now cast that pot of water on the ground."

The lad threw the pot of water on the ground, and it made such a vast ocean that the Devil could not get across it. The fox ran up again and said to the Devil:

"Start to drink the ocean dry!"

The Devil began to drink, but the water ran out of his rear end. And the fox said:

"I'll plug up your arse so that the water won't be able to run out of it."

"Plug it up, then," said the Devil.

The fox stuck a plug into the Devil's arse, but at last he said:

"It hurts so much, I can't hold on any more."

"Let go, then," said the Devil.

The fox let the plug fall out of the Devil's arse-hole, and all the water poured out and formed an ocean on the other side of him. And the Devil drowned in the ocean.

The horse took the lad to a King's palace. The lad went to the top of a mountain where there was a stable, and he led the horse in there. And the horse said:

"Go to that King, and ask him to give you work, and then keep me provided with food."

The lad went to the King, dressed up in the pigskin jacket that he had taken from the Devil's castle, and he asked if the King would take him into his service. The King said:

"Go and see the gardener, maybe he can put you to work, carrying away the rubbish."

The boy was engaged to carry the rubbish. He always wore his pigskin jacket, and so he came to be called Pigskin.

In the evenings he changed into the gorgeous costumes that he had taken from the Devil. On the first evening, he changed from his pigskin jacket into the star costume under the window of the King's youngest daughter, so that nobody except the Princess saw him. The King had three daughters. On the second evening, the lad changed into the moon costume, and on the third, into the sun costume, all on the same spot.

The Princess took such a fancy to Pigskin that she let him into her chamber. He visited her so often there that he caused her to grow heavy with child. When the King heard about this, he was so angry that he ordered Pigskin and the Princess to be put together to live in an old *sauna*, a bath-house. But Pigskin made that sauna so beautiful that the King had no single chamber more beautiful in the whole royal palace. And Pigskin continued to work as before, carrying the rubbish out of the garden, wearing his pigskin jacket.

Then war broke out. The other Princesses were being courted by great generals, and these went off to war. Pigskin went to the King and asked him for a horse, so that he could go to the war also. But the King said:

"What business has such a pig's hide in the war?"

All the same, he gave him a horse.

Pigskin asked to be allowed to go in advance, because he didn't know how to travel on horseback, and he was permitted to do so. He came to a bog and drove his horse into it. When the army came by, he began yanking his horse up out of the bog, and when the horse started kicking hard, he said:

"Kick as hard as you please, but we're going to war!"

"If you're still here when I return," said the King, "I'll have you shot at once!"

The lad pretended not to hear, and kept on trying to yank his horse out of the bog.

After the army had passed, he went up the mountain to the grey steed, and donned his star costume. He mounted the horse and rode through the air to the place where the King was. The King had suffered fairly bad losses, so that he had only a few men left. The lad rode out of the air straight in front of the King and said:

"Can I help Your Majesty?"

"You can, most surely," said the King.

The lad smote the air clockwise with his great sword. This made all the King's men revive. And when he smote the air counter-clockwise, all the King's foes fell. The King said to him:

"Gracious angel of the Lord, what reward would you like?"

And the lad replied: "The King's ring and handkerchief."

The King gave them to him, and he returned through the air to the top of the mountain, and left his steed and his star costume there. Then he went down to the bog again, to yank his other horse out of the quagmire. When the King rode up, he proposed to shoot Pigskin on the spot, but the generals protested, and said:

"Why should the King shoot a body like that when even an angel has come to his aid?"

So the King did not shoot.

After a while, war broke out again. The generals went off to the war, and Pigskin again went to the King to ask for a horse.

"What business has such a pig's hide in the war?" said the King. "You'll only ride the horse into a bog."

"The other was such a bad horse that it was impossible to get anywhere with it," answered Pigskin. "But let me have a better one."

14

The King gave Pigskin a better horse and a fairly good sword. Once more the lad asked to be allowed to ride in advance because he was a poor horseman, and this was permitted. Again he drove the horse into a bog. When the King rode up with his army, there was the lad, yanking his horse out of the quagmire; and when the horse started kicking, he said to it: "Stop kicking, we're on our way to war!"

"If you're still here when I come back," said the King, "I'll have you shot on the spot."

The lad acted as if he did not hear this, and kept on trying to yank his horse out of the bog. After the King had passed with his army, he went to his grey steed up on the mountain, and put on his moon costume. And he rode on his steed through the air straight to the place where the King was. The King had suffered such heavy losses once more that he had only a few men left, and he himself was on the verge of being taken prisoner by the enemy.

"Can I offer Your Majesty some help?" asked the lad.

"You certainly can!" said the King.

Once more he smote the air clockwise, causing all the King's men to revive. And he smote the air counter-clockwise, which caused all the King's foes to fall.

"How can I repay the gracious angel of the Lord?" asked the King.

"Let me have the King's hat," said the lad.

The King gave him his hat, and he again rode through the air to the top of the mountain. There he left his horse and his costume, and returned to the bog to yank the other horse out. When the King rode up on his way home, he made to shoot Pigskin, but the generals stopped him, saying:

"What does Your Majesty care about such a pig's hide, since the Lord's angel has helped you out for nothing?"

So the King did not shoot Pigskin.

Then a third war broke out, and it turned out to be the worst of all. Pigskin went once more to the King to ask for a horse.

"I'm not going to give you one," said the King, "since you've driven two of my horses into the bog already, and you'd certainly drive the third one into it too."

"Those two were so bad that it was impossible to get anywhere with them," said Pigskin, "but what about a better one?"

"Well, I suppose I must give you my best horse now," said the King, "but don't you drive it into the bog."

So Pigskin was given the King's best horse and sword, and he asked again to be allowed to ride on ahead. When he came to the bog, he steered his horse into it, as before, and was trying to yank it out when the King rode up with the army. When the horse kicked, he said:

"Go ahead and kick, but we're certainly going to join the war."

The King said: "If you're still here when I return from the war, I'll shoot you on the spot."

After the King had ridden on, Pigskin again went to the top of the mountain. He donned his sun costume, and steered his horse through the air to the place where the King was. By the time he arrived, all the King's men had already fallen, and the King himself had been taken prisoner.

"Can I help Your Majesty?" he asked.

"To be sure, you can," replied the King.

Then the lad smote the air clockwise, causing all the King's men to revive; and when he smote the air counter-clockwise, all the King's foes fell.

The King asked: "What would the Lord's gracious angel like as a reward this time?"

"The King's sword," replied the lad.

The King gave him his sword, and he rode off through the air to the mountain-top, where he left his horse and his costume. Then he went back to the bog, where he started to yank his other horse out of the quagmire. When the King came by, he wanted to shoot Pigskin on the spot, but the generals prevented him from doing so, saying:

"Why do you want to shoot a pig's hide like that after the Lord's angel has helped you out?"

So the King did not shoot him, but went to his palace, leaving Pigskin alone with his horse.

Then peace was made, and the King began to make preparations for his daughters' weddings. Two of the generals were going to marry the elder Princesses. When the wedding had already begun, the King told a maidservant to fetch Pigskin and his woman. The maid went, and knocked on the door of the sauna where Pigskin lived.

Pigskin's woman said: "I dare not let you in because Pigskin is asleep."

But the maid peeped through the keyhole, and inside, on the rear wall, she saw the star, moon, and sun costumes, and in the middle of the floor, a golden table, and on the table, the King's ring, handkerchief, hat, and sword. She ran back to the King and told him all she had seen in Pigskin's sauna, and she said that in the whole royal palace there was not a single chamber more beautiful than the sauna. The King

16

commanded that the very best horses be harnessed to the very best coach, and he went along himself as coachman to fetch Pigskin and his woman to the wedding. When the guests saw that the King himself took the coachman's seat, they all came out to welcome the party.

But everybody took fright when Pigskin came ahead of the coach, dressed in his pig's hide jacket, though behind him came his wife, wearing her best finery. When they stepped inside, Pigskin swept all the cinders on to the floor behind him with the pig's snout, and did a good deal of other mischief; but the King dared not say anything to him. A little while later, Pigskin disappeared, without anybody noticing him.

He went to his grey horse and changed into his sun costume. The horse said:

"Climb on my back, and we'll go to the King's feast together. Cut my throat, and take my head in your hand. Some blood will fall on your hand. Throw the blood into the lake by the castle, and go into it yourself for a little while. After you have come out, you will be met by a certain young man, and that will be me!"

Pigskin climbed on his steed's back and rode into the middle of the palace courtyard. He jumped down, cut the horse's throat, and took the blood into the lake, and only after that did he step inside the King's palace. All the guests came out to welcome him, and no lights were needed any more in the palace because he lit it up with his sun costume. After five minutes had passed, he went into the courtyard, and there he was greeted by a young man who said:

"I am the horse you killed, and I've turned back again into a human being. I am the King's son."

Then they went inside together. Great was the rejoicing when the King got back his son again. Pigskin received half the kingdom as his reward, and I went away from there.


## THE PRINCESS AND THE PEASANT

Once upon a time, near an ogre's cave, there was a house in which three brothers lived. The youngest was called Cindercock because he used to sit on the edge of the fireplace and rub his rear end in the cinders. From time to time, the ogres used to come out of their cave to steal hay from the brothers' barn. But at last the eldest brother decided that "It's high time I put an end to this stealing!"

4

One night, he went into the barn and hid himself under a pile of hay. Soon the ogres marched up to the barn, and the first to step inside said:

"If anybody comes, we'll kill him!"

When the lad hidden in the hay heard this, he was frightened and did not dare to move.

In the morning he went back to the house, where his brothers at once began to ask whether he had seen anything. When they heard that the thieves had appeared again, the second brother said:

"When I go there, nobody's going to do any stealing!"

That night, after the others had gone to bed, he went over to the barn to keep watch. Like his elder brother, he hid in the hay to wait. Once more the ogres came to the door of the barn, and the first to enter said:

"If anybody comes, we'll kill him!"

The boy, hearing such a threat, did not dare to move.

When he left the barn next morning and walked into the house, the others asked if the thieves had appeared. On hearing that they had visited the barn again, Cindercock said:

"It's my turn to stand watch, and now we'll finally get rid of them."

At nightfall he went to the barn and made a big haystack and hid himself in it. When the ogres came and their leader saw the ready-made haystack, he exclaimed: "We are lucky this time!" and he slung the stack across his shoulders. After carrying the burden for some distance, he had to stop for a rest. When the other ogres caught up with him, he said to them:

"There's surely a lot of hay in this stack, it's so heavy."

They resumed their journey. But from his hiding-place in the haystack, Cindercock boxed the ogre's ear. Terrible was the ogre's anger, and he scolded his comrades for daring to strike him. A little further on, the lad boxed the chief ogre's ear again. That angered him so much that he threw the haystack on the ground and warned his comrades, saying:

"If you do that just once more, I'll kill you, each and every one of you!"

He shouldered his burden again, but before long the boy smote him across the ears for the third time. Out came the ogre's sword, and he slew every one of his comrades. Having killed them all, he started off again by himself, but the boy took out his knife and slit the ogre's throat. Then he cut off the heads of all the ogres, and bound them together with a rope. Near the cave, he met the chief ogre's wife, and she said:

"Why, that's my husband's head you've got strung on that rope!"

"So it is," said the boy, "and I'll chop your head off too if you don't make up to me for all the hay your husband and the other ogres stole from my farm."

"Don't, dear boy!" she cried. "If you don't kill me, I'll give you a mouse-grey steed and a beautiful costume."

"Not good enough," said the lad, reaching for his sword.

"Don't, dear boy!" she cried again. "I'll give you a bronze steed and a beautiful costume if you spare my life."

"Not good enough," said the lad, thinking that, having already promised so much, she'd certainly give him more; and he made as if to pull out his sword.

"Don't, dear boy!" the old hag said, "I'll give you a steed of gold and a beautiful costume if you don't kill me."

"Only if you give me the whole cave will I let you live," said the boy.

Well, what could the old hag do but give the lad everything he asked for to keep him from killing her? After he had been given the cave, the horses, and the rest, he went back home, rejoicing. But he kept the ogres' heads himself, for he was afraid that, if the chief ogre's wife stuck her husband's head and body together again, the brute might return and take revenge for everything.

When he reached home, he flung the ogres' heads on the floor and said: "Serves you good and proper, you thieves!" Then he took the heads and stored them away somewhere. At any rate, the old hag never found them, for no ogres were seen round the brothers' house after that.

When some time had gone by, the King had it proclaimed in every parish church that the man who rode on horseback up the mountain on the top of which his daughter was seated in a splendid chair could win her hand, whoever he might be. The three brothers heard about this offer, and they, too, started off on horseback. The two older boys were each given a good horse to ride by their father, but the youngest had to set off on a poor hack. When his elder brothers had departed, he rode over to the cave. He entered and saw an old man, who said:

"What can I do for you, Sire?"

"Fetch me that mouse-grey steed and a decent suit of clothes."

Off went the old man, and soon returned, leading a mouse-grey horse, and carrying over his arm a splendid costume. The boy changed his clothes, and then mounted the steed. It did not take him long to reach the foot of the mountain, on top of which the King's daughter sat in a magnificent chair. Many an attempt had already been made, but nobody had succeeded in climbing very high, for the mountainside was so steep.

4·

When Cindercock noticed his father in the crowd, he went over to him and said:

"Mind my mitts for me, old man!"

Then he rode up the mountainside and got half way up, but at that point he had to turn back. He went to his father's side, took his mitts, and handed the old man ten gold pieces for having minded them for him. The old man did not recognize his own son.

The lad rode back to the cave and changed into his ordinary clothes. Then he hurried home and sat down on the edge of the fireplace, not minding the cinders that rubbed into his trousers. When his father and brothers returned, he asked straight away:

"And who won the Princess' hand?"

"Nobody," said the eldest brother, "but there was a certain gorgeously dressed gentleman who did manage to climb nearly half-way up the mountain on a mouse-grey horse."

"Yes," added his father, "and he gave me ten gold pieces."

A few days passed uneventfully, and then the King had it proclaimed again in church that any man who rode up to his daughter's side on horseback could have her for his spouse. On hearing this, the brothers mounted their horses for a new attempt. When they had gone, Cindercock rode over to his cave. The same old man was there to greet him, and as before, he asked:

"What can I do for you, Sire?"

"Fetch me the bronze-coloured steed and some good clothes," said the lad.

No sooner said than done, and the boy was on his way again. It did not take him long to reach his destination. Many a man had made the attempt before his arrival. Cindercock looked round for his father, and when he had found him, he said to him:

"Hold my mitts for me, old man!"

Then he rode up the mountainside once more, and came fairly close to the Princess. Nevertheless, he was forced to turn back before he reached the mountain-top. He rode to his father's side, took back his mitts, and handed over twenty pieces of gold. Soon he was back in his cave, changed into his own clothing, and hastened home before his father and brothers could get back. When they did return, he asked them:

"And who won the Princess' hand?"

"Nobody has won her yet," replied his eldest brother, "but one gentleman mounted on a bronze horse rode very close to her."

"Yes," added his father, "and he gave me twenty pieces of gold for minding his mitts."

Once more some days passed before the King made the same announcement as before, except that this time he promised half his kingdom, in addition to his daughter's hand, to the hero who rode up to the top of the mountain on horseback. The brothers decided to try their luck just once more. The two elder boys went off together as usual, leaving the youngest behind. But after their departure, Cindercock headed for his cave again. As before, he was met by the same old man, who said:

"What can I do for you, Sire?"

"Fetch me that golden steed and the most splendid costume in the wardrobe," said the boy.

Soon they were at hand, and the boy changed his clothes. Then he rode off. By the time he reached the mountain, many another lad had made the attempt to gain the Princess' hand, but all had failed. Seeing his father, the boy rode over to him and said:

"Mind my mitts for me, old man!"

Then he rode up the mountain and reached the Princess' side. And the Princess made a mark on the boy's forehead with her ring, so that she would always be able to recognize him.

After that, he rode down again and went to his father, took back his mitts, and handed the old man thirty gold pieces for minding them.

He wasted no time in taking the steed back to the cave and changing into his own clothes, and he got home before his father and brothers. When they returned, he asked at once:

"Who won the Princess' hand this time?"

"It was a certain gentleman who rode up the mountain on a golden horse," said the eldest brother.

"Yes," added his father, "and he handed me thirty pieces of gold."

Some days later, the King held a great feast in honour of the intrepid youth who had ridden up to the top of the mountain. But after waiting for many days without any sign of the youth, the King had a proclamation read in all the churches, commanding every man in the realm to come to the palace gate, so that the Princess could pick out the intrepid horseman. Men kept marching past the King's gate day after day, and the Princess kept looking at every forehead. Cindercock was the very last one to appear at the gate. Even though he was dressed in the clothes he had soiled by sitting in the cinders at the edge of the fireplace, and which were extremely ragged, the Princess cried at once: "He's the one!"

When the King saw what a ragamuffin the youth was, he felt deeply disappointed. Yet he kept his word. He beckoned Cindercock to follow him into a chamber where they could be alone, and there he offered the lad some money, so that he could buy himself better clothes. But Cindercock would not take the money, and then he went away.

After a while, there came riding into the palace yard a splendidly dressed gentleman, mounted on a golden steed. He greeted the King and told him he was none other than the rough fellow who, a short time before, had been clad in rags. That made the King's heart leap for joy, and he immediately set about arranging a great wedding at which Cindercock and the Princess were joined in marriage.

# SWEDEN

## THE RAT

Once upon a time there was a peasant who had three sons. Both the elder boys were very unkind to the youngest, and at such times the youngest boy left them and sat down at the hearth to poke in the ashes. The elder brothers therefore called him Ash-Peter.

One day the father called his sons and told them to go out into the world and find themselves brides to be brought home, together with the golden apples which their father had given them. Both the elder boys went at once to the stables, saddled their horses, and started off. But when the youngest brother came to the stables, he found only an old, weak horse. So he decided to walk, and he set out on his journey.

When he had walked quite a long way, he came to a forest. By this time it was already getting dark. Suddenly his golden apple, which he held in his hand, fell to the ground and began to roll. He ran after it, trying to catch it, but the apple just went on rolling and at last it was lost in a brier. The boy became very frightened. He looked round, and to his great astonishment, he found himself standing in front of a door. He tapped on the door and heard a voice telling him to come in. He entered and saw that nobody was at home. He sat down on a sofa by the wall, and began to cry bitterly. Then he saw a rat standing upon a table, and she asked him why he was crying. He said he was famished with hunger, and that he had lost a golden apple that had rolled away from him.

The rat said he need not cry, since she knew where the apple had gone to; and he would also get something to eat if only he would promise to take her as his bride. At first the boy pondered a little, but soon he promised to fulfill her wish. Then the rat called out: "All my handmaids, come hither!" At once so many small rats came out that the boy had to be very careful not to tread on them. They began to cook and be busy, and the big rat laid the table. The meal was soon ready, and then the big rat brought the golden apple and gave it to him, and invited him to sit down to dinner. When he had finished, she made a bed for him on the sofa and told him to go to bed. Next day the boy bade her farewell and started off on his homeward journey. The rat begged him not to forget her, and he promised that he wouldn't.

On his way home he heard the clatter of horses' hoofs behind him, and saw his brothers come riding up.

"Look at the Ash-boy!" they cried, as they rode by.

On reaching home, he took no notice of his brothers, but sat down to poke in the ashes. When asked where his bride was living, he answered that she lived in a brier hut in the forest. At that his brothers laughed scornfully.

Some time later the father again summoned his sons and said he would like to see what their brides could do, and therefore he wanted them each to bring him a cake of his bride's own making. Thereupon the sons started off, and Ash-Peter went to see the little rat. On entering the hut he greeted her, and she was very glad to see him again. Next morning Ash-Peter thought of his father's words, and he began to cry, for how could a rat be a pastry-cook? The rat asked him why he was crying, and he told her what his father had said. She told him not to cry, and then she called out:

"All my handmaids, come hither!"

All the small rats came out and at once made a fire, while the big rat prepared the dough. Soon the cake was ready. It was so fine that Ash-Peter had never seen anything like it. When he got home to his father, his brothers had already arrived. They showed their cakes, and they all thought them good and fine. But when they saw Ash-Peter's cake, they were ashamed; for it was both better and finer. And afterwards they said it must have been made by some old crone who did nothing but pastry-cooking.

After some time the father again summoned his sons and said:

"Now I have seen that your brides can make pastry, but I should like also to see if they can weave."

The boys did as they were told and set out again. When Ash-Peter reached the hut, he had his meal as usual, and then he went to bed. Next morning he thought of his father's words and began to cry. The rat asked him why he was crying, and he told her all about it. But she said he need not cry, for she would see to that. She called out:

"All my handmaids, come hither!"

There was a terrible din and hullabaloo that made him quite dizzy. Soon the fabric was ready, fine and white, the purest silk. The boy was delighted to see the fine material. He bade the rat farewell and went home again. His brothers were there before him, and were showing their fine cloths, but when they saw Ash-Peter's fine fabric, they were very much ashamed. And afterwards they said it must surely be the work of some old crone who did nothing but pastry-cooking and weaving.

Time went on, and then the father summoned his sons again and said: "Now I have seen that the brides can both weave and bake, but I also want to meet them, and see which of you has the finest bride."

The boys set out again. When Ash-Peter awoke next morning, he began to cry. He was thinking of his brothers coming home with their brides, while he came home with a poor rat. He told the rat all about his grief, and she said he need not cry. Then she called her handmaids and bade them dress her in all her rat-furs. They dressed her in a lot of rat-fur, and she looked like a big ball.

Next she ordered them to make a coach ready and put in the horses. They brought out a nutshell and harnessed eight chafers to it, and before the chafers there leapt fourteen fleas. Then the rat, with six smaller rats, seated herself in the nutshell, and on the driver's seat there sat a night-butterfly.

Off rolled the coach. When they came to a brook with a board over it, the rat handed a sword to the boy and begged him to cut off her head with it.

"How could I do that to you," he said, "who have been so kind to me?"

But he allowed himself to be persuaded by her prayers, and he did it. As he struck, the head of the rat tumbled into the brook, and on the other side of the stream, suddenly there stood a most beautiful princess, with six handmaids. The nutshell had been transformed into a glass coach, with mountings of gold; on the driver's seat a driver was sitting, and eight horses were harnessed to the coach. The fleas had been changed into fourteen halberdiers riding before the coach. Then the Princess clasped the boy in her arms and thanked him for having freed her from enchantment, and invited him to seat himself in the coach.

The brothers had already arrived home. They were standing in the courtyard boasting about their brides, when suddenly they heard the clatter of horses' hoofs and the rumbling of wheels on the highway. Then they saw a group of halberdiers come riding up, and after them a coach of glass and gold, glittering in the sunshine. When the carriage drew up, the Princess got out with Ash-Peter and the six handmaids. If ever anybody was astonished, the brothers were. They saw it was not difficult to tell which of them had the most beautiful bride. It was Ash-Peter. Then the wedding was held. It lasted long, and if it has not come to an end, it is still going on.

## THE INHERITANCE

Once upon a time there was a Lapp who had three sons. One day he said to them:

"I am not able to keep you in food and clothing any more. Now you must go out into the world and try to make your own fortune."

He then gave the eldest boy an old fiddle, the second a millstone, and the youngest only a bundle of flax.

The eldest son took his fiddle and went off wandering. At night he took shelter in a kiln. He climbed up on the tie-beams of the roof and began to play on the fiddle. When the wolves heard him fiddling, they came jumping over the threshold of the kiln. The boy shifted down from the beams and shut up the wolves. Again he began to play on his fiddle, and the wolves began to howl.

Then a traveller came by, and when he heard the howling and fiddling, he got off his sleigh to see what kind of fun they were having in the kiln. But when he opened the door, the wolves came dashing out. Then the boy came forward, seized the traveller by the collar, and said:

"What the devil have you been doing? Now you will be taken straight to Siberia! These animals were the wolves of the Russian Emperor, and I had undertaken the task of teaching them to play the fiddle."

The traveller was very frightened, and gave the boy many thousands of marks, hoping only to satisfy him.

The second son started off with the millstone round his neck. He walked and walked, and at length he came to a big forest. He could hear that there were already many people in the wood, so he climbed up a tall spruce, taking the millstone with him. Presently a crowd of robbers came by, and they sat down under the fir-tree, spreading out their things – gold and silver and all that they had of treasure.

They began to divide up the treasure between them. One said to another:

"You didn't show us everything you have got."

"If I didn't," said the other, "may God let fall a big millstone upon me!"

Then the boy quickly let go of his millstone. It fell right down among the robbers, who all of them plunged into the forest, and the boy wasted no time in gathering all their treasures.

The youngest brother had no choice but to take the main road. On his way, he thought: "I will make snares out of my bundle of flax, and go in for catching animals." And so he did.

At first he caught a squirrel, and put it in his bag. Next he caught a hare, and put that in his bag too.

26

At last he came to a marsh. While he was sitting there, on the fringe of the marsh, rippling his bundle of flax, the Water-Sprite sent his son to ask him what he was up to.

"Hullo, I am going to twine a stay-lace," answered the boy, "and then I shall pucker up the whole marsh like a tobacco-pouch."

"Don't do it," said the young Water-Sprite. "I shall go first and speak to the old man."

He did so. "There he sits scheming for the marsh to become dry," he said to his father.

"You used to be able to climb," said the Water-Sprite. "Can't you vie with him in climbing? Then you would get to see what he is worth."

The son did as he was told.

"Shall we have a climbing competition?" he asked the boy.

"Why should I bother to climb in competition with you?" said the boy. "But I have a little brother; you may try first with him. If he doesn't get the better of you, I can come next."

So saying, he opened the bag and let loose the squirrel, who flashed up into the top of a fir with a rattling noise. The young Water-Sprite scratched his head and went home.

"It wasn't worth trying," he told his father. "He had a little brother who flashed up to the top of the fir and set it rattling."

"You must tempt him to run a race with you," said the Water-Sprite. "Then we shall see."

The Water-Sprite's son went away again.

"Shall we run a race?" he asked.

"I don't want to bother myself with racing you," said the boy, "but I have a younger brother. If he cannot hold his own, I will come."

So saying, he opened the bag and let loose the hare. Off they ran. The hare ran like one possessed by the devil, and the young Water-Sprite could not keep up with him.

"It was rather so-so," he said when he was back home again.

"Well, then, you must wrestle with him," said his father. "You used to be a wrestler."

The young Water-Sprite did as he was told.

"Shall we try to wrestle?" he asked.

"I don't care to wrestle with you," said the boy. "But on the wooded hill up there you can see my old grandfather flaying a horse. Go and wrestle with him; if he cannot get the better of you, I will come. But he is a little deaf, so you must shout into his ear, 'Orr, orr, orr,' if he shouldn't be ready to hear you."

The young Water-Sprite did as he was told. When he got up the wooded hill, a bear was standing there, flaying a horse.

"Orr, orr, orr," said the young Water-Sprite.

"Orr, orr, orr," said the bear, but he didn't look up at all because he was busy eating.

"Orr, orr, orr," shouted the young Water-Sprite, somewhat louder.

"Orr, orr, orr," said the bear, and now he reared. He squeezed the young Water-Sprite till all his joints and muscles creaked and groaned.

"He is so terribly strong," said the young Water-Sprite when he was home again. "He didn't care to try himself either; but his old grandfather squeezed me so that I don't understand how I ever escaped."

"Now you must go and offer him money," said his father, "that he may not cord up the marsh."

The young Water-Sprite took a heavy load of treasure and gave it to the boy.

"That won't go a long way," said the boy.

Then the young Water-Sprite had to fetch another load.

"My father," he said, "sends you his respects, and asked me to let you know that he has to cut it pretty fine. If he must still pay more, we shall be utterly destitute."

"Well, if it must be," said the boy, who now had enough riches for his lifetime, "it'll do."

Thus the inheritance of the three sons was blessed.


## THE SILLY BOY

Once upon a time there was an old woman, who had one son. And since she lived in a forest, far away from people, the boy had grown up without learning anything, and he was so silly that, indeed, there was no end to it. Now he was getting on in years, and his mother began to worry and think that it wasn't right for him to be always hanging about at home.

"Oh dear! You are old now, and you ought to be of some use," she said.

She fetched a firkin of milk, put it into his hands, and told him to go out and sell it. When he asked her what price he was to demand for the firkin, she answered that he did not exactly need to sell it for money, but might be willing to accept something offered for it.

Well, off went the boy, and when he had gone some distance from home, he met a man who had needles to sell.

"What have you got in the firkin, my boy?" asked the man with the needles.

"I have milk," answered the boy.

"What am I to give you for it?" asked the tradesman.

"I take what I can get," answered the boy.

Well, the tradesman drank the milk and gave the boy some needles.

Now the silly boy thought he had discharged his duty. He started off on his way home, still carrying the needles in his hand. As he walked along, pondering what to do with the needles, he saw a man who had upset a hayload.

"Look here!" said the man, "you can help me with this hayload. I have upset it, and cannot manage to put it right alone."

"Well, I could do so," answered the boy, "if only I knew what to do with the needles I hold in my hand."

"Oh, can't you put them down somewhere?" said the man.

So the boy stuck the needles in the back of the hayload, and then he pulled, and hoy! ahoy! they heaved up the hayload. But when the hay was put right again the needles were gone, and it was futile to think of looking for them. Thus the silly boy had to resume his homeward journey without them.

Back home again, he met his mother.

"Well, my dear boy, what did you get for the milk?" asked the old woman.

"Why, I got needles, mother," answered the boy.

"That's very good," said the old woman. "Now I shall have some needles to mend your old clothes with, and I needn't buy any. But where are they?"

The boy told her he had stuck them into the hayload and lost them. Then the old woman said:

"How could you be so silly! You ought to have stuck them into the brim of your hat, then you would still have had them."

"Well," said the silly boy, "I shall do so next time."

Next time he was sent out with the firkin, he met a man who had whetstones and grindstones to sell.

"What shall it be for the milk, my boy?" asked the man.

"Oh, I take what I can get," answered the silly boy.

"Would you like to have a whetstone for it?" asked the man.

"Indeed I would," answered the silly boy, very pleased; and so the bargain was made.

Now he remembered his mother's advice, and he tried to stick the whetstone through the brim of his hat, but it couldn't be done. He had to content himself with putting it on the brim. And again he started off on his way home. On his way he had to pass over a bridge. There he stood, staring down into the water, looking for fishes, as he often did; and the whetstone fell into the water, as may be imagined. He couldn't get hold of it, and it was lost to him.

Well, on his arrival home, his mother asked him what he had got for the milk.

"A whetstone, mother," answered the silly boy.

"What luck!" cried the old woman. "Now we needn't borrow one when we want to whet our knives. But where is it?"

"Well," answered the boy, "I did as mother advised me to do." And he told her what had happened. The old woman said he ought to have put the whetstone in his pocket.

"Well," answered the boy, "I shall do so next time."

Next time he was sent out with the firkin, he met a man in a carriage. By the side of the mare there ran a tiny little foal.

"What am I to give you for the milk?" asked the man.

"I take what I can get," answered the boy.

"Would you like to have the foal?" asked the man.

"Certainly I would," answered the boy.

The man pulled up his mare, drank some of the milk, and gave the foal to the boy. Now the boy thought of his mother's advice, and he tried to put the foal in his pocket. He tried and tried, but it could not be done. He had to be content with thrusting its head into his pocket, and in that way he dragged the poor foal after him. On arriving home, he put the foal into the shed.

"Mother!" he cried, as he entered the cottage, "I have got a foal."

"Oh, how nice! How nice!" exclaimed the old woman. "We will bring him up, and when he is big and strong, we will go driving in a carriage to Christmas Matins, like other people. But where is the foal?"

"Well," said the boy, "he is lying in the shed."

"If he is lying, then I daresay he is dead," said the old woman. "Perhaps you have done something silly again."

"It may be," answered the boy, "but I did as mother advised me to do. I tried to put him in my pocket, and he may be dead."

And dead he was. The old woman was both sorry and angry, and she scolded the boy, saying:

30

"If you had had any common sense at all, you would have tied the colt to a gatepost, and put a wisp of hay before him, and then come to fetch me. I would have helped you, of course."

"Well," said the silly boy, "I will do so next time."

Next time he got a ham in exchange for the milk. He tied it to a gatepost and threw a wisp of hay over it, and then went to fetch his mother. When they got to the gatepost, the ham was gone, as you may imagine. The old woman was very upset, and at last she said:

"If you had at least put the ham on top of the gatepost, people would have supposed you had just gone in somewhere, and had put it there because you didn't want to take it with you to that place."

"Well, I shall do so next time," said the silly boy.

And so he did, for he put a piece of cloth that he had got for the milk upon the gatepost, and it blew away.

Now the old woman was in a quandary, and she felt that she couldn't put up with him any longer.

"I think," she said, "it's not worth while sending you to sell milk, for you just waste the milk and never bring anything home for it. If I could arrange for you to get married, I should be rid of you."

The silly boy thought that would not be a bad idea at all, so they went together, mother and son, to a village where the mother knew a girl.

They were well received and entertained, and in the evening, they had eggs for supper. It seemed as if the silly boy had never seen eggs before, for he thrust them into his mouth, shells and all. Everybody laughed at him, and the girl, seeing he was such a fathead, would have nothing to do with him. On their way home, his mother said:

"I don't wonder the girl wouldn't have you, since you behaved like that. You ought to have unshelled the egg, cut it into four slices, sprinkled it with salt, and eaten the slices one by one, and bread with them."

"Well, I will do so next time," answered the boy, as usual.

Next time they went courting in another place. There, too, they were invited to stay, and for supper they had peas. The boy began to divide his peas into four parts. He sat there, poor fool, cutting and cutting until late in the night, and he wouldn't let his mother disturb him, though she tried by all means in her power to make him stop. Things went as was to be expected, and that girl wouldn't have him either, as you may imagine. When he was to propose for the third time, the old woman, before entering the cottage, said to him:

"And you must know this much; if they invite us to stay to supper, we will decline."

31

They went into the cottage. The old woman spoke, and since her son was tolerably good-looking and was given no oppertunity to commit any blunder, that girl was promised to him.

Well, and then the wedding-day came. The old woman had first to go to the parson, and she had to dress the bride; but before going she warned the silly boy to behave himself properly. She told him to make the goat-bridge, for it was the custom to make such a bridge of twigs and leafy branches, to be put across the brooks for the use of goats and other small animals. And she added that at their wedding dinner he ought not to sit stolidly, but that now and then he should cast eyes[1] at his bride.

When the old woman had gone on her errands, the boy collected all his mother's goats, killed them, and laid them out to form a bridge. And he took out all their eyes. When he had finished, the old woman arrived with the bride. She saw at once that something had gone wrong. The bride asked her what was the idea of that queer bridge, and she answered that wolves must have been out and killed the goats. Later, when they were having their wedding-dinner, the boy took out his goats' eyes, and began to throw them at the bride, one by one. She wondered what was the meaning of this. At first she thought it was just some kind of pleasantry of her husband's; but presently she was hit by a goat's eye, and then by another, and another, and the boy sat there goggling with the same stolid face. "This won't do," she thought, "I'll run away from it all"; but it couldn't be done, for the boy followed hard on her heels all day.

She thought she would run away when night came, and so she asked her husband's permission to go out. But he was suspicious, and he wouldn't allow her to go out unless he could bind her by the arm, so as to pull her in again should she stay away too long. So he took her garters and his own, tied them together, and fastened them to her arm. After a time, as she did not come back, he began to haul and haul. The sound of somebody coming, and of a scraping on the floor was heard. When the bride was near him, he clutched at her, and got hold of two curious things.

"Mother! Mother!" he cried, "the bride has horns!"

"Oh, shut up, you fool, it's only her tresses," answered the old woman. Again he seized the bride.

"Mother! Mother! the bride has a beard!" cried he.

---

1. In Swedish, "to cast eyes" at somebody means to glance gently at the person concerned. Cf. also pp. 83–84 below.

"Oh, you fool, I think it's her back hair," answered his mother.

But then it began to bleat, and the old woman saw that it was her last goat, which was still alive, and which had been fastened to the garters by the bride.

Well, now the silly boy set off in pursuit of his bride, but she already had a good start, and so he had to drive. When she saw that he was coming after her, she stood in the middle of the road, and there was a white gleam about her, for in her hurry she had not dressed at all. The silly boy took her for a dead tree, so he returned home to fetch an axe. The bride gained the lead again, and the silly boy lost his bride, and he never got another. Thus the old woman had to put up with her silly son, who became a proverb. You will often hear people say: "To act like the silly boy" or "To cast eyes like the silly boy", and similar sayings.


## THE GIANT'S TREASURE

Once upon a time there was a crofter and his wife who had three sons. The two elder boys were able and manly, and they were always working with their father. But the youngest preferred to stay at home and help his mother with her tasks.

The crofter and his wife died, and the sons had to divide the property. The two elder boys divided it all between themselves. Only an old kneading-trough was left, and this, they thought, would fit the youngest brother who was so fond of baking. The youngest brother, content with this division, took his kneading-trough and went down to the lake. There he made oars out of some sticks, pushed the kneading-trough out on to the water, and sat in it. He was tossed up and down by the waves, and he sang and had a good time. When he had had enough of being idle, he rowed over to the royal castle, where he was allowed to stay and lend a hand at such jobs as he could.

The King's daughter, the Princess, was very beautiful, and she had many suitors. But the King had said that he who wished to marry her must first steal the giant's treasures and make her a present of them. Many people had tried to steal these treasures, but all had been devoured by the giant.

When the boy heard about this, he went to the King and asked that he too might be allowed to try. The King laughed at him, but the boy persisted. At last he got the King's permission to try. Then he stuffed

5

pebbles into his little bag which he always carried with him, climbed into his kneading-trough, and rowed over to the other side of the lake where the giant had his home. There he crept near the house, wondering how he could make shift to steal the giant's treasures, which consisted of a golden sword, three golden hens, a golden lantern, and a golden harp.

As he stood there pondering, he saw the giant going to the granary, where he began to thresh. The boy climbed to the roof of the granary, and made a little hole through which he could peep down. Presently he took a pebble out of bis bag and let it fall upon the sword, which resounded.

"What is the matter?" burst out the giant, "I am not angry now." For the golden sword had the peculiarity that it resounded every time the giant was out of temper. Presently the boy dropped another pebble on the sword, and after a while, one more. The giant grew angry with the sword, which resounded every time, so he unbuckled it. He threw it outside the granary door, saying:

"Lie there till I have finished my threshing."

Then the boy quickly climbed down, took the sword, ran down with it to the lake, and rowed over to the other shore, where he hid it well.

Some days later he again rowed to the giant's home. This time he had grain in his bag. When he had crept near to the place, he saw the golden hens picking there. He began clucking to them very softly, and lured them right down to the boat, where he tied them with limebast. Then he rowed over to the other shore, and hid the golden hens as carefully as he had hidden the sword.

A few days later he again rowed to the giant's home. This time he had salt in his bag. He lay in wait all day without catching a glimpse of the golden lantern, or of the golden harp. When evening came, he saw the giant's wife put a big cooking-pot on the fire, and he stealthily threw one clod of salt after another into it. When the giant's wife had cooked her porridge, she dished it up. Now it was time for the giant to have his supper. But at the very first mouthful, he made a wry face and asked his wife what kind of porridge she had cooked that night. The wife said it was just the ordinary porridge; but the giant answered that she had better taste it herself, to see whether she would like to eat it. So she did, and she found that the porridge was not fit to eat, so salty it was. But when she went to prepare another potful of porridge, she had no more water. So she lit the golden lantern, took the bucket, and went to the well to fetch some water. While she drew it up, she put the lantern down by the well-head. Then the boy sprang at her and threw her into the well, after which he took the lantern, ran down to the lake, and rowed across with it to hide it on the other shore.

The giant began to wonder what had become of his wife, as she was so long coming back. He went down to the well, and there he saw his lantern gleaming far off on the lake. But he had to help his wife out of the well, and meanwhile, the boy escaped with the lantern. The giant determined that the harp should not be taken by anybody, so he locked it up with twelve padlocks, and went on guard to catch the boy, if he should come back.

Some days later the boy ventured to row over once more to the giant's home in order to steal the last of his treasures. But scarcely had he landed when the giant caught him, and locked him up in a pigsty. There he was put on a fattening diet, eating nuts and milk fresh from the cow. When he was fat enough, the giant intended to eat him.

One day the giant came to the pigsty and told the boy to stick out his finger through a hole in the wall. Instead, the boy stuck out an alder-peg, newly peeled. The giant cut into it, thinking it was his finger; but finding the flesh too hard, he told his wife to give the boy still more milk and nuts. A little later, he came again to the sty and told the boy to stick out his finger. This time the lad stuck out a cabbage-stalk. Now the giant thought the boy's flesh was tender enough to make a feast of him, so he ordered his wife to light a fire and roast the boy. He himself went away to invite the guests.

As soon as the oven was hot, the giant's wife fetched the boy, who had fattened well on the rich food. She told him to sit down on the grid-iron, and he did so; but when the giant's wife wanted to shove him into the oven, he tumbled down. This was repeated several times. At last the giant's wife got angry and pushed him down; and to show him how to sit properly, she sat down herself, squatting on the grid-iron. Then the boy seized it quickly, shoved it into the oven, and locked the shutter. Next, he stuffed straw into her fur coat and put it on the bed, so as to look as though the giant's wife herself was lying there. Then he unlocked the twelve padlocks, took the harp, and went down to the kneading-trough boat. He rowed away over the lake, playing the harp as he went.

Presently the giant came home. When he saw the fur coat on the bed, he thought it was quite all right for his wife to take a rest before the arrival of the guests. But as she never offered to get up, he decided to rouse her from sleep. Then he saw there was nothing but the fur coat on the bed. He flew into a rage, and opening the shutter, he saw his wife sitting dead in the oven. He jumped up and ran in a rage down to the

5·

lake; and there, far off, he saw the boy sitting in his boat, rocked by the waves. He threw himself down by the lake and began to take long draughts, so that the water of the lake sank rapidly, and the boy was drawn nearer and nearer to him. But the giant had drunk more than he could carry, and suddenly he burst.

So the boy was saved. He landed and took the treasures from their hiding-place. He carried the lantern in his hand, and girded himself with the sword. He clucked to the hens to follow him, and went playing on the harp to the King's castle. The King received him with great joy, and the wedding was held with joy and happiness. And the Princess and the boy, who in the end became King of the country, lived long and happily together.

# NORWAY

## SALENTO AND SØLENTO

Once there was a King whose wife only gave birth to girl-babies. The King was very distressed about this because he desired a son with all his heart. But on his lands there was a cottar[1] whose wife only gave birth to boy-babies. One day the King had to go on a long journey, and before he left he told the Queen that if she had a girl-baby before he came home, she was to kill it. The Queen knew she could never have anything but girl-babies, and so, as you might expect, she was very sad and unhappy.

The King went off. A little while afterwards, the Queen had a fine little girl-baby, who was so lovely that she nearly went out of her mind every time she thought it would have to be killed. But finally she thought of what she must do. She went to the cottar's wife, who had just had a baby-boy, and they agreed to exchange the babies, but secretly, so that the King would never know about it. The cottar's wife thought it a fine thing that a poor woman like herself should have a son who would rise to be a prince, and to have in his place the King's daughter to raise. So she and the Queen exchanged babies; both were happy about it, but the Queen was the happier of the two. She called her boy Salento, and the cottar's wife, who didn't want to be outshone, made up a similar name and called the girl Sølento.

Long after long, the King came home, and when he heard that his Queen had had a baby-boy, he was happier than he had ever been before. As he and the cottar's wife lived quite near each other, it so happened that the Prince and the cottar's daughter played together; and in order that the two children should be even happier than they were, the King gave them each a colt. The girl's colt was called Greybell, and was a good horse.

When a long time had passed, and the Prince and the cottar's daughter were nearly grown up, they loved one another dearly; but the King didn't

---

1. Cottar: a peasant occupying a cottage on a farm, and working on the farm at a fixed rate when required.

like that. Day in and day out he thought how he could separate Salento and Sølento, for he felt it would be a bad thing if the Prince lowered himself so far as to take a poor cottar's daughter for his wife. He turned it over in his mind for a long time, and finally he decided to send Salento far, far away to another land and, while the boy was away, to take Sølento and bury her alive in a big mound.

No sooner said than done. Salento was sent away, and soon after, the King ordered his servants to dig a deep hole in a big mound. They made a fine room deep in the mound; and the King gave them a lot of food and clothes, mead and wine, and all sorts of good things which he told them to put in the room. Then Sølento and her two dogs were brought there and put into the room, and the King's servants filled up the hole again with earth as fast and as well as they could.

When Salento came home again, he missed Sølento at once. He searched for her for many days, but no Sølento could he find. He became so downhearted and full of longing that he could find no peace in his homeland, but went out into the wide world to see if he could find a girl who looked like his old sweetheart, Sølento. He travelled for many years and went through many kingdoms, and finally he found a girl who looked very like Sølento. It wasn't difficult for him to make an agreement with her, and then he was just as happy as he had been before, and even more so; for the girl he had found was uncommonly rich. He asked for her hand and took her away with him, and off he went home again as fast as he could.

The King was astounded when he saw his son coming with such a woman, but Salento said she was his sweetheart. Then the King asked where he had found such a sweetheart. Salento replied that he had found her in a land far away in the world, and that she was so rich, and owned so much gold and silver, that he didn't think the King would say no to their marriage. The King answered that he thought it would be a sin and a shame to say no to such a marriage. So now there was life and bustle in the King's homestead. They brewed and got ready in every way for the wedding-feast.

The day came when Salento was to marry his rich bride. It was seven years since Sølento had been buried in the mound. For seven years the dogs she had with her had been digging a hole, and finally they got out, exactly on the day of Salento's wedding. Now Sølento, too, was saved. She climbed out of the mound and went to the King's homestead, where the wedding was. She went to the cook in the kitchen, who said she could be a kitchenmaid, to carry wood and water, and do other

menial tasks. Soon afterwards, the bride came down to the kitchen.
She didn't know what to do, because she was having the pains of childbirth and couldn't go to the church. The kitchenmaid and the bride
were so like each other that it wasn't long before the cook, who was a
quickwitted woman, hit upon a plan. The kitchenmaid should dress herself in the bride's wedding clothes, and go with the bridegroom to church
in the bride's place. But she mustn't speak when she met the bridegroom.
The kitchenmaid was willing to do this, but only if she could have the
horse Greybell, which was in the King's stable, and ride on it to church.
The bride was so desperate that she did not dare say no; so she ran
to the King and asked if she could ride to church on Greybell. Although
the King did not want to deny the rich bride anything she wanted, he
said at first that he dared not let Greybell out of the stable because the
horse hadn't been out under the open sky for seven years. The bride was
cut to the heart when she heard this; but she begged so long and so
nicely that she finally got permission to ride to church on Greybell. Then
she went back to the kitchen and told the kitchenmaid she could have
Greybell for her ride to church. So the wedding-dress was brought to
the maid, and she was dressed up in the finest way, just like a bride.

The King's servants took Greybell out of the stable, and when the
maid saw him, she talked to him and said:

"Fall on your knees, Greybell, while the rich young bride lies in the
stable and gives birth to young, small foals."

When Greybell heard her speak, he recognised Sølento, and he fell on
his knees in front of her so that she could mount.

So Salento and Sølento rode to church, and on the way they passed
a maple tree.

> "Here you stand, maple, with your leaves so gay,
> Where Sølento and Salento happily used to play,"

said Sølento as they rode past the tree.

"What did you say?" asked the bridegroom, who was riding ahead.

"Oh, I'm just talking to my horse," said the maid.

So they rode on farther, and they came to the mound where the maid
had been buried, and there stood two pigs rooting in the earth.

> "Here you stand and root, you swine,
> Where before there has been both mead and wine,"

said Sølento.

"What did you say?" asked the bridegroom.

39

"I was just talking to my horse," said Sølento.

When they had ridden for some way further, Sølento dropped one of her gloves. The bridegroom saw this, and jumped down to pick it up. On it were sewn the names Salento and Sølento, and when he saw them, he was filled with wonder.

When they came back to the King's homestead, the bridegroom locked himself into a room. After a while his sweetheart, who had been having the pains of childbirth, came and knocked on the door, and wanted to come in to him.

"You can't come in unless you tell me what it was that you said when we rode by the big maple," he said.

The rich girl knew nothing about that; but she ran back to the kitchen and asked the kitchenmaid why she had spoken to the bridegroom, and what it was she said when they rode by the maple.

"I just talked to my horse," said the maid.

"Well, what was it you said then?" asked the rich girl.

"Oh, I said

> Here you stand, maple, with your leaves so gay,
> Where Sølento and Salento happily used to play,"

said the kitchenmaid.

The rich girl went back to the bridegroom, knocked on the door, and asked again to come in; but he answered that she could not come in unless she was willing to tell him what it was she had said when they rode past the maple.

"I said,

> Here you stand, maple, with your leaves so gay,
> Where Sølento and Salento happily used to play,"

said the rich girl.

"But you still can't come in unless you tell me what it was you said when we rode by the mound," said the bridegroom.

The rich girl stood there, knowing nothing about that; so she ran back to the kitchen and asked the kitchenmaid what she had said by the mound.

"Oh, I said

> Here you stand and root, you swine,
> Where before there has been both mead and wine,"

said the kitchenmaid.

The rich girl went back to the bridegroom again and told him what the kitchenmaid had told her; but the bridegroom said she still couldn't come in unless she brought him the mate to the glove she had dropped. Now she stood there, knowing nothing about that; but she ran back to the kitchen once more and asked the kitchenmaid if she had dropped a glove on the way to the church.

"Yes, I did," said the kitchenmaid.

"Oh, please," said the girl, "I've got to have the mate to the glove you dropped, and take it to the bridegroom. He wants to have it so very much."

"I'll go myself," said the kitchenmaid; and she went to the bridegroom with the glove. When he saw that it was his first sweetheart with whom he had been to church, he was happier than he had ever been in his life before. But as for the rich girl, they threw her into the snake pit.

## THE ANIMAL SONS-IN-LAW

Once upon a time there was a man who had three daughters. When they grew up, the first was going to marry a ram and the second a bumble-bee, but the third was going to marry an otter. They were to have their weddings in turn, the eldest first and then the others. When the time came for the eldest daughter to marry the ram, the man and his wife set off to the wedding-party, which was to be held in the ram's house. Later in the day, the man's wife began to wonder what they would have for supper, for she was very curious, as women often are.

"You'll see," answered the ram.

The best thing they could do was to hang up the kettle in the fire-place. So they did. And the ram began to butt so that meal fell and dropped into the kettle. Porridge was the only thing they had to eat at this wedding-party.

So the man and his wife set off for the wedding of the daughter who was going to marry the bumble-bee. It went just the same; when some time had passed, the man's wife wanted to know what they would have for dinner.

"Porridge," answered the bumble-bee.

"Yes, but you haven't any milk to go with the porridge," said the man's wife.

The bumble-bee answered that he would take care of that himself, and that the best thing they could do was to cook the porridge. When those in charge of the cooking heard that, they made the porridge and ladled it out on to the plates. They thought the bumble-bee must have a plan. Well, the bumble-bee took the plates and set them all in a row on the table, and then he flew on to a shelf above them and dropped honey down on the porridge. The wedding guests ate it and just raved about it.

Then the man and his wife went to the wedding of the daughter who was going to marry the otter. They hadn't been there very long before the wife wanted to know what they were going to have for dinner.

"Oh, we'll have something to eat," answered the otter, and he said that if the man would come along to the ocean, he'd see.

The man was willing to go with him at once. They climbed into the boat; the man sat amidships and rowed, and the otter sat in the stern, facing him, and helped. They rowed out a good way, and then the otter sprang up and asked the man if he could see whether his eyes were green. No, the man couldn't say that. So they rowed further on, and again the otter sprang up and asked the man if he could see whether his eyes were green. No-o, the man wasn't quite sure. So they rowed on a long way, so far that the man didn't dare go any farther. The otter sprang up again and asked the man if he could see now that his eyes were green. Yes, said the man, now his eyes had turned green. He dared not say anything else. Then the otter said they had come out far enough. Now they were going to fish.

"I'll jump into the sea; but as soon as you see bubbles coming up, you must hurry and help me," said the otter.

The man promised to do that, and the otter jumped out. A long time went by, and the man began to think the otter wouldn't come up. But finally he saw some bubbles coming up, and he rowed over to them as fast as he could. There was the otter coming up with a big salmon. So they rowed to land and had a good time at the wedding-party; nobody complained about the food at that party. Then the man and his wife went home.

It wasn't long before the wife began to worry about what they were going to have to eat.

"Pooh, there's always a way," said the man.

Now he had learned so much that they would never have to do without food.

"Hang up the kettle, woman," he said.

He went out and found two big ram's horns, and began to butt against the mantel over the porridge-kettle, which hung from the pothanger. But all he got that time was soot porridge, and that didn't fill them up. Then the wife asked what they could have with it. Oh, the man said, he had learned so much that he could surely find a way for that too. The only thing she had to do was to set the porridge-bowls on the table. So she did. The man crawled up on to the long shelf they had over the table and began to throw up on the porridge. He thought he could certainly spit up honey just as well as the bumble-bee.

The next day the woman began to worry about what they would have for dinner; she didn't know what she could manage.

"Oh ho!" said the man, "that isn't hard. We'll just row out to sea."

Well, they climbed into the boat. The woman sat amidships and rowed, and the man sat in the stern, facing her, and helped. They rowed out some way, and then the man sprang up and asked her if she could see whether his eyes were green. She was angry; she thought he was making fun of her. She said she couldn't see any green in his eyes. So they went on rowing. After a while he sprang up again, and asked her if she could see now that his eyes were green. She wasn't any more pleased; she said he should stop talking nonsense, because he was as green in his eyes as any one else. So they rowed on a long way; he didn't say anything, and she didn't either. Suddenly he sprang up and asked if his eyes were green now. The woman was very angry. Certainly he was green, she said; he was as green as he could be.

"Aha! When bubbles begin to come up behind the boat, you must hurry and row there," said the man.

And so saying, he dived into the sea. But no bubbles came up, and no man came up either. The woman waited there, and she rowed and rowed, and looked for the bubbles that were supposed to come up.

And she's there still.

## STRONG PETER AND HIS MEN

An old woman had a son who grew very fast, and his name was Peter. He ate up all his mother's cows and sheep. One day she said to him:

"Now you must go away, my boy. I can't feed you any longer."

So he left the house and walked for a while. Presently a man came towards him, and Strong Peter asked him:

"What's your name?"

"My name is Hill-Carrier."

"Let's be partners," said Strong Peter.

They walked on for a while. Then another man came towards them, and Strong Peter asked him:

"What's your name?"

"Well, Steel-Squeezer."

Peter said: "Let's try our strength." Then he threw him down, and said: "Let's be partners."

So now they were three. They went on for a while and came to a mountain with a door. They heard hammering inside the mountain. Strong Peter said to Steel-Squeezer:

"Open the door!"

Well, he couldn't open it, so Peter said to Hill-Carrier:

"You try!"

He couldn't open it either. Then Strong Peter pulled as hard as he could, and the door opened. They went in, and found a giant hammering there. Peter wanted to help with the hammering, and the giant gave him a big hammer. Strong Peter said:

"I can't move it a bit."

Then the giant took a horn of strength and let Peter drink from it, and after that, he could handle the hammer a little better. He said:

"I still can't move it."

So the giant let him have a drink from another horn, and then he could handle it very well. He said:

"Haven't you an even better horn of strength?"

The giant took another horn of strength and gave it to him. He began to hammer. The giant blinked his eyes every time Strong Peter swung the hammer. Then Peter hit the giant on the forehead with the hammer, so that his head broke in two, and he died. Strong Peter took the horns of strength and drank them all.

They went on farther and came to a forest. They found a kettle there. They were hungry, and Strong Peter said:

"We'll hunt animals in the forest so that we can cook some food."

They went hunting in the forest, and they weren't there long. Then they began to cook. Strong Peter told Steel-Squeezer to watch the kettle while they went out after animals and got another kettleful. When the kettle began to boil and the food was nearly ready, a threeheaded troll came and said:

"Let me eat from the kettle."

He ate all the food. When Strong Peter came back from the forest, he asked who had emptied the kettle. Steel-Squeezer said:

"A troll with three heads came and ate the food."

Then Strong Peter told Hill-Carrier to watch the kettle. The other two went out into the forest. When the kettle was boiling and the food was nearly done, a troll with six heads came and ate up everything. The two returned from the forest, and Strong Peter asked who had emptied the kettle. Hill-Carrier said:

"A troll with six heads came and ate the food."

Strong Peter sent the other two into the forest and stayed behind himself to cook. When the kettle was boiling and the food was nearly ready, a troll with nine heads came from the forest and began to eat the food. Strong Peter sprang up, pulled a birch tree up by the roots, and struck off all the troll's heads. Then he went to the forest and shouted. The two others came back and found the food ready; they ate it, and then they cooked another kettleful and they ate that.

They went off again and walked for a long time. Presently they heard hammering under the earth. Strong Peter went to the place where the sound came from, and saw a giant making heads for his son.

"Tramps knocked my son's heads off," said the giant, and he asked Strong Peter to help him. Peter tried, but he couldn't lift the hammer, so the giant let him take a drink from the horn of strength, and after that, he could lift the hammer, but only just.

"Haven't you another horn of strength?" he asked.

"I've got another," said the giant, "and I'll give you some from it."

Strong Peter took a drink from it and began to hammer. The giant looked on. Then Peter grabbed the hammer and hit the giant on the forehead and killed him, after which he went to the corner, killed the son, and emptied both the horns of strength.

The three wandered on and came to a King's homestead. The King engaged them as servants. They began to work, and he sent them to the forest with horses. In the forest they made such huge loads of wood that the horses couldn't pull them. So they cut the horses' heads off, put them on the loads, and pulled them home. Then the King was frightened, and they ate up all his horses, cows, steers, sheep, everything.

The King saw he couldn't feed them, so he said:

"Go and bring back Asterekjempen's[1] sword."

---

1. Asterekjempe: a kjempe is a giant or a great warrior.

They sailed to Asterekjempen's farm. Strong Peter set Steel-Squeezer to watch the ship during the night. He said to him:

"If any one comes and asks what the ship is loaded with, you must say 'That's none of your business'."

Steel-Squeezer saw a boat come rowing out from the land with a boiling kettle amidships. Asterekjempen's son came on board the ship and asked:

"What's the ship loaded with?"

"That's none of your business," said Steel-Squeezer.

Then Asterekjempen's son took him and threw him into the boiling kettle, and rowed to land.

The next night came. Peter set Hill-Carrier to watch the ship, and he said:

"If any one comes and asks what the ship is loaded with, just say 'That's none of your business'."

Presently a boat came rowing out from the land and up to the ship. Asterekjempen's son asked:

"What's the ship loaded with?"

"That's none of your business," said Hill-Carrier.

Then Asterekjempen's son fought with him, and threw him into the boiling kettle, and rowed to land.

A third night came. Strong Peter went to watch himself. He saw a boat come rowing out from the land. Asterekjempen's son asked:

"What's the ship loaded with?"

Strong Peter said very gruffly: "That's none of your business."

They began to fight. Strong Peter fell down on one knee, but he got up again and threw Asterekjempen's son down, and made him answer his questions:

"When does your father sleep most heavily, when does he sleep not so hard, and when does he sleep most lightly?"

Asterekjempen's son said:

"He sleeps most lightly when a white smoke comes out of his mouth, and when green smoke comes out, he's not sleeping so hard. But when red smoke comes out, he's sleeping most heavily."

Then Strong Peter threw Asterekjempen's son into the boiling kettle.

Night came. He went on land and looked through Asterekjempen's window. He saw white smoke coming out of his mouth. A little while later, green smoke came out. He waited for a while, and then red smoke began to come out. He crept into the house, went over to the bed, took hold of the sword quietly, went out, boarded the ship, and rowed off. When morning came, Asterekjempen noticed that the sword was gone and the ship had left. He went up the mountain and looked far out over the ocean. He took a horn and began to drink the sea dry. He drank so much that it began to be dry behind the rudder. Strong Peter rowed so hard that the iron oars bent. But then Asterekjempen's horn burst, the ocean ran out again, and Asterekjempen died.


## BUTTER BALL SPA

Once there was a woman who had a boy named Butter Ball Spa. And she also had a dog called Speedy. One day the dog barked so fiercely that the mother said:

"You must look, Butter Ball, and see who's coming."

The boy went out, and he said:

"There's a man coming with a bag on his back, and a hat on his head, and a staff in his hand. Where can I hide?"

"Hide under my baking table," she said.

Then the man came in.

"Good day!" he said. "There's a good fire burning in the oven. Is Butter Ball Spa at home today?"

"No," said the mother, "he's out with his father in the forest cutting wood today."

"Oh, that's really a shame," said the man. "I've got two fine silver spoons I wanted to give him."

"Peep, peep, here I am!" said Butter Ball under the baking table.

"You'll have to take them out of my bag yourself," said the man, "because I've got such a pain in my back that I can't bend over."

Well, the boy did it. And the man took him, put him in the bag, and tied the cords; then he went off with him.

When he had gone some way, he had to go and relieve himself. The boy said:

"You must go many miles away from the road, or else I'll burst from the smell."

So he did. When Butter Ball was alone, he took out a knife that he had and cut a hole in the bag. Then he filled it full of small stones, and ran off home.

The troll came back; he took up the bag and went home to his wife, Kettle.

"Now I've really caught something fine," he said, "I've got a boy, and he's thick and fat."

But when he went to empty him out, there were only small stones rolling out on the floor. He was very angry, and the next day he went out again. When he came to the woman's house, Speedy began to bark very fiercely, so she said:

"You must look out, Butter Ball, and see who's coming."

So the boy went out, and he said:

"There's a man coming with a bag on his back, and a hat on his head, and a staff in his hand. Where can I hide?"

"Hide under my baking table," said his mother.

The troll came in.

"Good day!" he said. "There's a good fire burning in the oven. Is Butter Ball Spa at home today?"

"No," said the mother, "he's out with his father in the forest cutting wood today."

"Oh, that's really a shame," he said, "I've got two fine silver forks I wanted to give him."

"Peep, peep, here I am!" said Butter Ball under the baking table.

"You'll have to take them out of the bag yourself," said the man, "because I've got such a pain in my back that I can't bend over."

Well, the boy did it; and so the man took him, put him in the bag, and tied the cords; then he went off with him.

This time he didn't have to stop, but took Butter Ball straight home to Kettle. They put him in the cellar for fourteen days. They fed him. Then he stuck out his forefinger, and it was as skinny as a dry cornstalk. So they fed him for fourteen more days. Then he stuck out his finger, and it was as thick as a chopping-block. Now he was fat enough, and they were going to slaughter him. The troll put him into the room and went away himself.

Kettle found a big axe and came into the room with it. But Butter Ball Spa got the axe away from her, and he ran out, slammed the door, climbed up on to the roof, and lay down and looked down through the smoke-hole.

"Where are you, Butter Ball Spa?" said Kettle.

"Butter Ball Spa's sitting up on the roof," he said.

But just as she was going to look up, he dropped the axe on her head and killed her.

Then he cooked some porridge. And he took her hind end and stuck it into the middle of the porridge as a butter eye. After that, he ran up on to the roof again, with the axe.

After a while, the old troll himself came in and hollered:

"Kettle, where are you?"

"Kettle's in the well."

So the troll bent down to look into the well in the cellar, and just then Butter Ball dropped the axe on to his head. And the troll tumbled into the well.

And if he hasn't come up out of it yet, he's there still.

# ICELAND

## THE STORY OF PRINCE HLINI

There was once a King and a Queen in a certain kingdom. The King's name was Ring, but it is not told what his Queen was called. They had a son who was called Hlini. He began early to show promise, and was held to be a man of great courage.

The story tells that a certain peasant and his wife lived in a cottage. They had a daughter whose name was Signy.

One day the Prince went hunting with his father's courtiers. When they had hunted down a number of animals and birds and were about to go home again such a thick fog came down and they lost sight of the Prince. They searched for him a long time, but couldn't find him, so they turned homewards. When they came to the palace they said that they had lost Hlini and could not find him anywhere. The King was very upset at this news, and next day he sent many men to look for his son. They searched the whole day until evening, but they didn't find him, and so it turned out on the three successive days of the search; Hlini was not found. The King was so sorrowful that he took to his bed like a sick man. And he had it announced that whoever found his son and brought him back home should win half the kingdom.

Signy, the cottager's daughter, heard of the disappearance of the Prince, and also of the reward his father had promised if Hlini were found. So she went to her parents and asked them for food for a journey and new shoes, and then she set out to look for the Prince. Now there is this to tell concerning Signy's travels that when she had been walking the greater part of the day she came, towards evening, to a cave. She went inside, and saw there two beds; on one was a quilt of cloth-of-silver, on the other a quilt of cloth-of-gold. She had a better look round, and saw the Prince lying in the bed with the cloth-of-gold quilt; she tried to wake him, but she couldn't. Then she noticed that some runes were written on the bed which she did not understand. After that she went out to the entrance of the cave and hid behind the door. When she had been in this hiding-place a little while she heard an enormous din outside, and saw two coarse-featured troll-wives coming into the cave. As soon as they were inside, one of them said:

"Fi Fo Fum! Man-smell in our cave!"

But the other said it was only from the Prince, Hlini. Then they went to the bed the Prince was sleeping in and said:

> "Sing, O sing, O swans of mine,
> So that Hlini wakes."

The swans sang, and Hlini awoke. The younger troll-wife asked him if he didn't want anything to eat; but he said No. Then she asked him if he would marry her. He flatly refused. So then she raised her voice and said:

> "Sing, O sing, O swans of mine,
> So that Hlini sleeps."

The swans sang and he went to sleep. The troll-wives lay down in the bed with the cloth-of-silver quilt. In the morning when they woke, they roused Hlini and invited him to eat; but he would not. The younger one again asked him if he would marry her; but he refused as before. So they sent him back to sleep in the same way as last time, and afterwards they went away out of the cave.

When they had been gone a little while, Signy came out from her hiding-place and woke the Prince in the same way as the troll-wives. She greeted him, and he replied in a friendly manner, and asked her for news from home. She told him everything, and all about the grief his father was suffering for his sake. Then she asked him what had been happening to him. He told her that as soon as he had become separated from his father's courtiers he had met two troll-wives, and they had brought him to this place. One of them intended to force him to marry her, as Signy had heard, but he always refused.

"Now," said Signy, "when the troll-wife asks you this evening if you will marry her, you must agree on condition that she tells you what is written on the beds, and what they do in the day-time."

This seemed to the Prince an excellent plan. He took up a chequer-board and invited Signy to play chequers with him, and they played until evening. But when it began to get dark, she sent him back to sleep and went into her hiding-place. A little later she heard the troll-wives come striding into the cave with bundles of dead fowls. They lit a fire, and the elder one began to dish out the food; but the younger one went over to the bed and woke Hlini, and asked him if he wanted to eat. He said Yes.

6·

When he had finished she asked him if he would marry her. He said he would if she told him what the runes on the bed meant. She replied that they read:

"Run, O run, O bed of mine,
Wheresoe'er I will."

He was pleased at this, but he said she would have to do more than that to get what she wanted. She must tell him what they did out in the forest in the day-time. She answered that they went out hunting animals and birds; but in between doing that, they would sit under a certain oak and throw their life-egg to each other. He asked if there was any danger in handling it, and the troll-wife said it mustn't be broken, for then they would both be dead. The Prince said it was good of her to tell him this, but that now he wanted to rest until morning. So she said he should have his way, and sent him back to sleep. In the morning she woke him up to eat, and he accepted the food. Then she asked him if he would go into the forest with them that day; but he answered that he would rather stay at home. Thereupon she bade him goodbye and sent him to sleep, and with that, the two troll-wives went away.

Now, when they had been gone a fair time, Signy woke the Prince and told him to get up.

"We will go out into the forest," she said, "to where the troll-wives are. You must take your lance with you, and as soon as they begin to throw the life-egg to each other, you must throw the lance at the egg; but your life is at stake if you don't hit it."

This seemed to the Prince an excellent plan. They both got up on to the bed and chanted:

"Run, O run, O bed of mine,
Out into the forest."

The bed set off with them both and didn't stop until it was out in the forest by a certain oak. There they heard a lot of loud laughter. Signy told the Prince to climb up into the oak, and he did so. He saw the two troll-wives under the oak; one of them was holding a golden egg and throwing it to the other. At that moment the Prince threw his lance, and it hit the egg in mid-air, so that it broke. At this, the troll-wives were so overcome that they fell to the ground and foamed at the mouth. Then the Prince came down from the oak, and he and Signy went back to the cave on the bed in the same way as before. They took everything of value in the cave and filled both beds with it, after which they each

52

climbed on to one of the beds and chanted the runes. So the beds trundled off home to the cottage with them and all the treasures.

The peasant and his wife welcomed them and invited them to stay with them; they accepted, and stayed there overnight. Early next morning Signy went to the palace, approached the King, and hailed him. He asked who she was. She said she was a peasant's daughter from a poor cottage, and asked how he would reward her if she managed to bring his son safely home. The King said there was no point in answering that, for she would scarcely be able to find the Prince when none of his men had succeeded. Signy then asked whether he would not let her have the same reward as he had promised others, if she did manage to find his son. He replied that it should be so.

So Signy went back home to the cottage and asked the Prince to go with her to the palace. He did this, and she took him straight into the palace and up to the King, who welcomed his son and told him to sit down on his right and tell him all that had happened from the time that he became separated from his companions. The Prince sat on the throne next to his father and asked Signy to sit on his other side, and then he told the story just as it had happened, and said that this woman, by freeing him from the hands of the trolls, had saved his life.

When he had finished, Hlini got up, stood in front of his father, and asked him to let him take this girl as his wife. The King willingly gave his consent, and straightway arranged for a feast to which he invited all the nobles in his kingdom. The wedding celebrations lasted a week, and when they were ended everyone went home, praising the liberality of the King who had sent them away with fine gifts. And Signy and the Prince loved each other deeply and for many years. With this, the story ends.

## WAKE-WELL AND HIS BROTHERS

Once there was a peasant and his wife. They had five sons, and there was a year between each of them. No one else lived in the cottage besides this couple and their sons. Once, as on many other occasions, the father and mother went out to the fields to mow hay, and left the brothers behind at home, alone; for at this time they were old enough to be left on their own without harm. The weather was fine that day, and the brothers were playing around the farm. An ancient and decrepit old woman came to them. She asked the boys to give her something to drink, and they did so. When she had quenched her thirst she thanked them kindly and asked what their names were. The brothers said they had no names. Then the old woman said:

"I was very glad to get a drink from you, for I was dying of thirst; but I am now so poor that I can't reward you properly. But still, I am going to give you each a name. The eldest shall be called Wake-well, the second Hold-well, the third Cut-well, the fourth Track-well, and the fifth Climb-well. I give you these names in return for the drink, and I hope they will turn out to be right."

Then she said goodbye to them, and told them to remember the names carefully. She went on her way. In the evening when the boys' parents came home they asked if any one had come during the day. The brothers told them what had happened and all about the names which the old woman had given them. The peasant and his wife said they were pleased about this.

The brothers grew up with their parents until they were grown men. Then they said they wanted to go away from the cottage and seek their fortune elsewhere. Their parents gave them permission. So they set out, and nothing is told of their travels until they came to the King. They asked him for a winter's lodging and said they wanted it either for all of them or else for none of them. The King said they could stay with him for the winter if they were willing to watch over and guard his daughters on Christmas night. They agreed, and so they all stayed with the King.

Now the position was this. The King had had five daughters. But on the last two Christmas nights two of them had vanished, one on each night, from their bower, even though there had been someone watching over them. No one knew how they had disappeared, and they could not be found anywhere, in spite of all the expeditions and searches which the King had had made. When the brothers heard how things were, they asked the King to have a new bower made, very strongly built, and in a separate building.

Now Christmas came. The three Princesses who were left went into the bower, and all five brothers with them. They intended to keep watch over the Princesses throughout the night; but they all went to sleep, except Wake-well. There was a lamp burning, and the bower was firmly locked. During the first part of the night Wake-well saw a shadow come to one of the bower windows, and soon afterwards, a horribly big and monstrous hand stretched in over the bed of one of the Princesses. Then Wake-well quickly woke up his brothers, and Hold-well grasped the paw that was stretching in, so that the person it belonged to could not pull

54

it back, though he struggled to do so. Then Cut-well came and cut off the hand against the window-frame. The person outside ran away, and the brothers chased him. Track-well was able to follow the tracks, and finally they came to some very steep cliffs which no one could scale except Climb-well. He climbed up the cliff, threw a rope down to his brothers, and pulled them all up. They found themselves at the mouth of a great cave. They went in, and there they saw a troll-wife; she was weeping. They asked her what was the matter with her. She was reluctant to tell them at first, but in the end she did so. She said that during the night her husband had lost one of his hands, and this was why she was so upset. The brothers told her to cheer up and get hold of herself; for they could cure her husband.

"But no one may watch us," they said, "while we are carrying out the cure. We are so careful with our secret knowledge that we tie up any one who is near, so that no one can come to us while the cure is going on; for much depends on this."

They offered to cure the troll-wife's husband right away, if she would let them tie her up. She wasn't very keen on this, but finally she let herself be persuaded. So they tied her up tightly, and then they went in, along the cave, to her husband. He was the most horrible troll, and they didn't beat about the bush, but killed him straight away. This done, they went back to the troll-wife and killed her. They searched the cave but found nothing of value that they wanted to take away with them. Nor did they notice any more trolls there. But while they were searching they came upon a little side-cave opening off the main one, and when they went into it they saw both the lost Princesses there. They were chained up; one of them had plenty of flesh on her, but the other was only skin and bone. They were bemoaning their fate, and the plumper one was saying that she was to die today; for the trolls were going to have her for their Christmas dinner. But at that moment, the brothers went in and freed them, and told what had happened. Then the sisters cheered up, as one might expect, and the brothers took them home to the palace and put them in the bower with their sisters. The day had not yet dawned.

But when morning came the King went to the bower to see how the brothers had succeeded in guarding the Princesses. And when he heard everything that had happened during the night and saw all his daughters reunited there, he was so happy that he could scarcely contain himself for joy. Then he prepared an enormous feast, and that feast ended with each of the brothers celebrating his wedding with one of the King's daughters. Afterwards, the brothers all became very great men, and they lived good and long lives, in the greatest good fortune.

And now the story is over.


## THE STORY OF HILD THE GOOD STEPMOTHER

Once there was a King and a Queen in a certain kingdom. There was only one thing to spoil their happiness – that they had not been granted any children. The King had a counsellor whose name was Rufus: he was disliked by nearly everyone except the King and the Queen. He was the Queen's constant companion, and he was always with her wherever she went.

One fine day when there was snow on the ground, the Queen went driving on a sledge, and Rufus was with her. She became very hot on the sledge so that her nose bled, and she let the blood drip on to the snow. She told Rufus she wished she had a daughter whose complexion was as beautifully red and white as the blood on the snow. Rufus said her wish would be fulfilled; but yet the first time she set eyes on her daughter, she would not be able to avoid putting a spell on her which would compel her to burn her father's palace, have a baby before she was married, and kill a man. The Queen was willing to do anything to get a daughter, and when some time had passed it became evident that she was with child. Eventually the time came for her to be brought to bed, and all went well. But as soon as she heard the midwives say she had given birth to a beautiful baby girl, she begged them earnestly to take the child away from her as quickly as possible, because she didn't want to look at it. The midwives thought this very strange, but they took the baby to the King and told him what the Queen had said. He thought his daughter promised to be amazingly beautiful; he had her christened and called Ingibjörg, and then he sent her away to foster-parents in another part of the kingdom, a long way from the palace.

The Queen soon recovered in the normal way, and no one noticed that anything was wrong. The King often asked her to go with him to see their daughter, or to let the child come to them. But the Queen would not allow either. She said she could not see her daughter, but she did not say what would come of it if she did.

So time passed until Ingibjörg was ten years old, and so beautiful and promising that many people remarked on it. About this time, the Queen contracted a serious illness, which she thought would bring about her death. So she sent for Ingibjörg, for she felt she had to see her, in spite of everything, before she died. When the girl arrived the Queen sent everyone out of the room where she lay, so that she could talk to her daughter in private. Ingibjörg came in and bent over her mother, intending to embrace her; but the Queen pushed her away, and laid on her the spell to which she was doomed, and which has already been described. After that, the Queen died, and Ingibjörg fainted away; she was still unconscious when the Queen's people came into the room. Everyone was amazed at what had happened. With careful nursing, Ingibjörg soon recovered; but she was very upset and sorrowful about her fate, though everyone thought this was because of the loss of her mother.

The King too was full of grief for a long time. He deeply mourned the Queen, and paid little attention to the government of his realm. He had a friend in his kingdom whom he trusted more than any one else because he had long proved himself to be a good and loyal counsellor. This man, when he heard of the King's neglect of affairs of state, set out to visit him. The King welcomed him, and was very glad to see him. Then this friend pointed out to him that continual sorrow and neglect of state affairs did him no good, and it would be much better for him to take another wife. Though his loss had been great, he could best forget his sorrows by choosing another Queen in place of the one who was dead. At first the King was reluctant to do this. He didn't want to hear any more about it, and said that second wives seldom turned out well. But his friend pressed the matter all the harder, and offered to go himself to find a wife who would be a consolation to him; he would, he said, choose him a wife no less carefully than if he were choosing for himself. So the King, because he trusted his friend better than any one else, allowed himself to be persuaded by his arguments.

The ambassador set out, and searched far and wide. He went to many kingdoms and saw princesses and noble ladies, but by no one was he so taken that he wished to make a proposal on behalf of his friend, the King. At last he heard of a certain Princess whose name was Hild. He was told that she was very like Princess Ingibjörg in appearance, and that her father ruled over a certain island. So the ambassador sailed there and, on leaving his ship, he went before the King and told him for what purpose he had come. The King said he would make no decision until he knew his daughter's wishes. He told the ambassador to wait in the hall till she came, so that he could be sure he had no secret words with her meanwhile, and then he was to make the proposal to her himself when she arrived.

The ambassador did as he was told, and waited until the tables were set up in the hall. Then a door at the side opened, and the Princess came in, with her maids-in-waiting, went up to her father, and bowed to him. The ambassador looked at her, and she seemed to him both fair and courteous, and very like Ingibjörg in appearance. He went up to the King and his daughter, made his speech, and asked for her hand on behalf of his own King. The King of the island said he had heard only good reports of the ambassador's King, but that his daughter must make up her own mind whether she wanted to betroth herself to him. The Princess said she would willingly accept the match that was offered to her, and she would go back with the ambassador, but that the engagement was to last for three years, because she was still young and largely inexperienced. The ambassador said he could promise this on behalf of his King; and so it was agreed that, on this condition, the Princess should be betrothed to the King.

Another ship was got ready for her journey, and she and the ambassador sailed away together. When the King saw them coming, he went down to the shore with his daughter and his courtiers to receive his Queen-to-be. He was straight away captured by her beauty; and everyone was amazed to see how alike were the Princess Ingibjörg and Hild, they being so distantly related. It was soon obvious also that they would get on very well together.

They all went to the palace, and the King wanted to celebrate his marriage with Hild immediately. But his friend said he could not do that, for Hild had consented to be betrothed to him only on condition that the engagement should last three years. The King agreed to this.

Hild had not been there very long before she asked him to have a separate bower built for herself and Ingibjörg. She said she expected that they would soon become good friends, and that it would be best for them both to be as near each other as possible. This was done, and they both went to live in the bower. The two friends got on wonderfully well, so that even their wishes always ran together.

When some time had passed Ingibjörg began to be much quieter than before. Hild asked her what was making her unhappy and urged her to speak out; but Ingibjörg would not tell her. Then Hild said there was no need for her to ask about the matter, for she knew that she was under a spell that would compel her to burn her father's palace. The Princess admitted that this was true, and she was in a terrible dilemma because of it. Hild told her not to worry, they would find some way out.

Towards the end of the summer, the King went away to collect the taxes from his land, and about the same time everyone left the palace to go far and wide in search of apples. But Hild and Ingibjörg remained at home. Then Hild said that now they must take everything valuable out of the palace, and burn it while it was empty of people. They did this, and set fire to the palace in many places so that the fire spread over it in a very short time. When the people who were out apple-picking saw great flames coming from the palace they turned homewards, to try and save it. But when Hild and Ingibjörg saw them coming they took buckets and poured pitch on the fire as hard as they could, so that there was no chance of stopping the fire, even if all the palace men came to help. So it came about that the palace was burnt to ashes, and nothing could be done about it. Hild said that since this accident had happened, it was no good being idle. Everyone must start to build a palace in another place, and anyway, it was not such a great loss that the old palace had been burnt, for it had been so ugly that she could never have enjoyed being there for long.

So now all was hurry and bustle. They began work on the new palace, and put as much craftsmanship into it as they could. It was finished by the time the King came home, and was much more beautiful than the old one. The King was amazed at the change, and Hild told him about the accident that had happened to the old building, and begged him not to be angry with her for having the new palace built in its place, for she could never have lived with him in the old one. The King thought the new palace was so beautiful that he thanked Hild for the improvement that had been made to his home.

When the second year came round Ingibjörg again became sad, and wouldn't tell Hild, much less any one else, what was making her unhappy. Everything went as before; Hild guessed that now the time was coming when Ingibjörg would be compelled to have a baby before she was married, and Ingibjörg said this was true, and that she now had absolutely no idea what to do.

"We shall not die without trying something," said Hild. "You must go out into the forest. There is a certain house there, and you must stay in it for three nights; a man will come to you there, and you must do as he says. After that, you must come back home, and I will see to it that no disgrace falls on you because of this."

Then Ingibjörg went and was away for the time that had been arranged. Some time later Rufus went to the King and said he had a difficult matter to discuss with him. The King asked what it was, and Rufus replied that, though he might think it unlikely, his daughter was then with child.

The King told him not to talk such nonsense, for that was beyond belief. Rufus said he had not expected to be believed, but that the King could test the truth of the matter by laying his head in Ingibjörg's lap when he went to the friends' bower on Saturday, and seeing whether he didn't find something amiss.

On the Friday before the King was going to the bower for this purpose, Hild warned Ingibjörg that Rufus had told her father she was going to have a baby, and had advised him to put the matter to the test in the way already mentioned. At this, Ingibjörg became so frightened that she was quite overcome. Hild comforted her, and said:

"You must take the puppies away from our dog, wrap them up in a cloth, and put them under your apron. When the King notices the kicking of the puppies, he will think that what Rufus says is true. Then you must stand up and drop the puppies from under your apron, so that he sees."

Soon Saturday came, and the King went to the friends in the bower, as was his custom every Saturday. Ingibjörg did just as Hild told her. The King laid his head in her lap, and jumped back rather quickly when he felt the movement under his head. He asked her if she was going to have a baby. She did not reply, but stood up and dropped the puppies from under her apron. Then the King thought he understood what was what; he went to Rufus and was very angry with him for his wickedness and his slander against his daughter. He said he deserved to be slain, but that he would spare him because his late Queen had been so fond of him. Rufus said he had been telling the truth all the same, but that here there were tricks in the game which were concealed from the King. The conversation was then dropped for the time being, but later on, Rufus suggested that the King should get a doctor to examine some of Ingibjörg's blood, to see whether she was a virgin. The King could cut her a little on the hand, and pretend it was an accident; and thus he could obtain the blood and give it to the doctor to find the answer. The King answered that there was no need for him to make this test, because he trusted his daughter absolutely; but yet, perhaps he might do this.

Now it went as before. Hild knew what the King intended to do in the bower on the next Saturday, and she told Ingibjörg, who was just as frightened as before; but Hild said:

"We shall not die without trying something. We will sit next to each other and hold hands when the King comes; and when he cuts you, I shall move my hand against the edge of the knife and let a few drops of my blood drip on to your lap, and then wrap a cloth round my hand.

Then you must give your father your apron with my blood on it; but be careful not to let any drops of your own blood fall on to it."

Everything went according to plan. Hild moved her hand against the edge of the knife just as the King cut Ingibjörg, let the blood drip on to her lap, and then wrapped a cloth round her hand. The King asked Ingibjörg to take off her bloodstained apron and give it to him. She did so, and he took it to the doctor and bade him examine the blood. It then turned out that it was from an untouched virgin. The King was now even angrier with Rufus than before, but he let matters stand for the time being.

Time passed until the King's birthday. Then Rufus told him that now it would be proved that what he had said was true; for Ingibjörg was accustomed to dance the whole night through then, but she wouldn't do so this time, and he could take that as a sign. Hild knew of this plan of Rufus', and she said to Ingibjörg that, as it had long been said they were so alike, they must now exchange places and clothes. Ingibjörg must sit by the King during the night and pretend to be Hild, and she would dance in her place. So it came about, as the story-books say, that they each played their part. The Ingibjörg who was really Hild danced the whole night; towards morning, she had danced everyone off the floor and was left standing there alone, and then she said she wished the dance was only just beginning. But the King sat by Ingibjörg, thinking she was his betrothed, and feeling very pleased that Rufus had again been proved a liar.

After this, he rebuked Rufus, and said it was not because of any virtue in himself, but because of the former Queen, that he was not slain as a slanderer and a liar. But Rufus said his words would prove to be true, even if it were only later on.

Soon the time came for Ingibjörg to be brought to bed. Hild got a room ready for them both on the highest floor of the bower, and herself acted as midwife for Ingibjörg, letting no one else come in. She swaddled the baby, and put a three-stringed necklace of her own round its neck, and put it out on the bower wall. After that, she stayed with Ingibjörg all the time, and allowed no one to come in, not even the King, saying that Ingibjörg felt so ill that she could not bear any moving about or chattering. After a fortnight, Ingibjörg got up and went about again. She was somewhat paler than before, but Hild said this was due to long lying in bed, and everyone believed her.

Some time later, when Ingibjörg had completely recovered, so deep a depression came over her that she was almost beside herself. Then all

61

happened as usual. Hild guessed what was making her unhappy, that now she must kill a man. Ingibjörg said this was the reason, and that she was inconsolable and at her wit's end at the thought of it. Hild told her not to worry; for again they would find some way out.

Soon the time came round for the people to go out in search of apples. It happened that in one place there was a great tall apple-tree growing halfway down the sea-cliffs; the apples on this were the finest and the biggest, and someone had to be let down to it on a rope. No one dared to do this except Rufus. So now Hild suggested that they should go with the King when Rufus was being let down the cliff; Ingibjörg was to ask her father to let her hold the rope, and she was to lose her grip on it, so that Rufus fell to his death, for it would be fitting that his wickedness should fall on his own head. But Ingibjörg said she could never bring herself to do such a thing. Then Hild said she would take hold of the rope with her, at first. So it was decided between them. Ingibjörg asked her father to let her hold the rope when Rufus was let down the cliffside, to see how strong she was. The King let her do as she wished; both Hild and Ingibjörg took hold of the rope, but Hild quickly let go of it, and Ingibjörg a little later. And that was the death of Rufus. The two friends pretended that this accident was a terrible blow to them, so that the King should not be angry with them, but most people were well pleased that Rufus was dead, for everyone had some grudge against him.

So the next winter went by, and then the King arranged for his wedding feast and married Hild. She sat on his right, and Ingibjörg on his left. When evening came, there was a knocking at the door, and Hild said she ought to receive the guests. She went to the door, and the guest came into the hall to meet her, and straight away, she fell on his neck and kissed him. The King began to get rather annoyed; but Hild took the newcomer up to him and said he was her brother. Then she took him to Ingibjörg and told her this was the man she had slept with in the hut in the forest, and he was the father of her baby. The King was not very pleased at this news, but Hild went out of the hall, and came back a little later with a baby of about a year old in her arms. She gave it to Ingibjörg and said it was her own, and Ingibjörg recognized the necklace round its neck, and knew that what Hild said must be true. Then Hild told the King the whole story of the evil spell that had been laid on his daughter, and how she had escaped from her difficulties. She also said that a spell had been laid on her brother, that he should be a monster in the daytime, but a man at night, and that he should never escape from this enchantment until some Princess was willing to free him from it by sleeping with him on three successive nights. Then Ingibjörg had lifted the spell from him, and had borne his baby, and in return Hild had helped her.

After this, Queen Hild's brother asked for Ingibjörg's hand in marriage, and this was willingly granted, both by her and by the King. The feast was extended, and both weddings were celebrated together.

So ends the story of Hild the good stepmother.

# DENMARK

## KING WIVERN

There was a King who had a very beautiful Queen. But on the morrow of their wedding, it was found written on their bed that they were to have no children. The King was much grieved by that, but the Queen was even more so. One day, when she was walking by herself in deep thought, she met an old hag, who asked her whether she might be allowed to know the Queen's grief. The Queen looked up and said:

"Oh, it's no good telling you. It's not a thing in which you can help me."

"Oh, it might be, after all," said the hag, and she begged her to say what it was.

Well, the Queen could tell her then, indeed she could. She told her how on her wedding-night it had been written on her bed that she was to have no children, and it was this that made her so sad.

"Well, to be sure, I can give advice for that, and tell you what to do in order to have children," said the hag. "Tonight, when the sun is setting, you must take an earthen mug and put it upside down in the north-western corner of the garden, and next morning at sunrise, you must take it back again. You will find two roses under the mug, a red one and a white. If you take the red rose and eat it, you will have a son; if you take the white one, you will have a daughter. But you must not take both of them."

The Queen did as she had been advised. In the morning, when the sun was rising, she went down there and took away the mug, and there were two roses under it, a red one and a white. Now she did not know which to eat. If she took the red one, it would be a boy; he would go to the wars and be killed, and then she would have no children just the same. So she decided to take the white rose. It would be a girl, who would stay at home with her parents, and later get married and have another kingdom. She ate the white rose, but it tasted so good that she took the red one too; for she thought to herself that if she were to have twins, that would not be so bad either.

Now, about this time, she was very distressed because the King had to go to the war. After a while, she felt that she was with child. She wrote to the King to let him know; and of course, he was very glad.

Time went by, and the day of childbirth came. She was delivered of a wivern. No sooner had he been born than he dug himself down under the bed in the room, and there he stayed. After a while, a letter came from the King to say that he was on his way home. On the day that he drove into the courtyard in his coach, and the Queen came out to welcome him, the wivern, too, came to meet him. He jumped up by the side of the coach and said:

"Welcome home again, father!"

"Eh? Am I your father?"

"Yes, if you will not be my father, I'll shatter both you and the castle!"

So the King had to agree. They went inside, and the Queen had to confess what had happened between her and the hag.

A few days later, the whole council and all the magnates of the realm assembled to welcome the King and congratulate him on his victory over his enemies. The wivern, too, came up, and he said:

"Now I'll marry, father!"

"Well, who do you think will have you?"

"If you do not find me a wife, young or old, big or small, rich or poor, I'll shatter both you and the castle!"

The King had to write to all the neighbouring kingdoms to ask if anybody would have his son. A very beautiful Princess came; but she thought it strange that she was never allowed to see the one she was to marry before they entered the hall where the wedding was to be celebrated. Then the wivern came up and stood by her side. The wedding-day came to an end, and they went to the bedroom. But no sooner had they entered the room than he shattered her.

Time went by, and after a while, the King's birthday came round. When they were all sitting at table, the wivern once more came up and said:

"Now I'll marry, father!"

"Who do you think will have you now?" asked the King.

"Well, if you do not find me a wife, young or old, big or small, rich or poor, I'll shatter both you and the castle!"

The King wrote to many kingdoms to ask if anybody would have his son. Again there came a Princess, but she shared the same fate as the first.

Then the Queen's birthday came round, and again the wivern came up and said:

"Now I'll marry, father!"

7

"I cannot find you any more wives. Now the two mighty Kings whose daughters I found you as wives will wage war on me, and what am I to do with them?"

"Well, let them come! As long as you have me as your friend, they can come, even if there were ten of them. But if you do not find me a wife, young or old, big or small, rich or poor, I'll shatter both you and your castle."

The King had to give his promise, but he was much grieved. Now, on the land there was an old man who was a shepherd. He had a little cottage in the wood, and a daughter. The King went to him and said:

"Look here, my good man, won't you give your daughter to my son?"

"Oh, no, I can't do that. I have only this one daughter to support me in my old age. And I think it too hard on her. For since he would not spare such lovely Princesses, he will not spare her either."

But the King would have it, and the old man had to put up with it. He went home and told his daughter. She became very unhappy, and in deep thought she vent to the wood to pick wild apples and berries. An old woman came up to her. She, too, had come to the wood to pick wild berries and apples. She wore a red skirt and a blue bodice.

"What makes you so sad?" asked the old woman.

"To be sure, I have good reason to be sad, but it's no use telling you about it, for it is not a thing in which you can help me."

"It might be, though," answered the old woman. "Tell me!"

"Well, I am to be married to the King's son, and he is a wivern. He has shattered two princesses. My father had to promise the King that he should have me, and now I know that he will shatter me too."

"Oh, I think there may be a remedy for that, if you will do as I tell you."

Well, she would. So the old woman said:

"When you are to stand before the priest with him, and they know that you are coming with him to the bridal chamber, you must wear ten shifts. If you have not got so many, you must borrow them. When you go into the chamber with him, you must demand a tubful of vinegar and a tubful of whole milk, and as many birches as a man can carry in his arms. And it must all be brought into the chamber. As soon as he enters, he will say: 'Fair maiden, shed a shift!' Then you must say: 'King Wivern, shed a slough!' He will go on saying this to you, and you answering him, until he has cast off his nine sloughs, and you have cast off your nine shifts. Then he will not have any more, but you will still have one left. Next you must seize hold of him; he will be nothing but

66

a bloody lump of flesh. You must dip the birches in the vinegar, and beat him for as long as you think he can hang together. After that you must wash him in the milk, wrap him in the nine shifts, and put him on your arm. But when you have both lain down, you must fall asleep, be it ever so little."

The girl thanked her for her teaching, yet she was afraid. It was hard to have to deal with such a cruel animal.

The wedding-day arrived, and they came to fetch her, driving in a coach so grand and smart. There were two ladies in it, who dressed her as the finest of brides. When she entered the hall, the wivern came up and stood by her side, and they were married.

When night was falling, and they were to go to the chamber, she demanded a tubful of vinegar, a tubful of whole milk, and an armful of birches. The gentlemen made fun of her, calling it boorish tomfoolery and fancy; but the King said she was to have what she demanded. Before she entered the chamber, she put the nine shifts over the one she was already wearing. Thereupon they entered the chamber, and the wivern said:

"Fair maiden, shed a shift!"

"King Wivern, shed a slough!" said she.

"Fair maiden, shed a shift!"

"King Wivern, shed a slough!"

And so they went on until she had cast off her nine shifts, and he his nine sloughs. There he lay on the floor and could hardly stir, and the blood was running off him. Now she took courage, seized the birches and dipped them in vinegar, and beat him with all her might until only bits and stumps were left of the birches. Next she washed him in the milk, wrapped him in the nine shifts, and went to bed with him in her arms. It was long before she could sleep, but at last she dropped off. When she woke up again, she was lying in the arms of a handsome Prince.

In the morning, they dared not go to look in through the door of the bridal chamber, for they thought she had shared the fate of the Princesses. But the King would go there, anyhow, to have a look inside. When he opened the door, she said: "Come in! All is well."

He went in, and great was his delight. He fetched the Queen and all the others, and there were such congratulations over that bridal bed that the like had never been seen before. Presently the servants came, and the two got out of bed and went to another room, for that chamber, you see, did not look well. Then there were wedding festivities once

7ᐧ

more, with joy and merriment. And the King and Queen loved the bride so much that they could not do enough for her, because she had saved their son.

After a time she was with child. But a war began, and both the old King and King Wivern had to be off. In the fullness of time she was delivered of two lovely boys.

At that time the Red Knight was serving there. He was sent with a letter to King Wivern to say his wife had borne him two boys. When the Red Knight had gone some distance, he opened the letter and wrote another, saying that she had given birth to two puppies. The King read that letter and was very distressed. He marvelled that she should have borne puppies, for he had feared she might bear some kind of serpent. He wrote back to say that they must, by all means, let live whatever she had borne, could it only live, until his return. But when the Red Knight had travelled some distance with that letter, he destroyed it and wrote another, saying they must burn both her and her offspring

The Queen was much grieved by this letter, for she was so fond of her daughter-in-law. After a time, a letter came from King Wivern to let them know when he would be back. Then they took fright, and were at a loss to know what to do. The old Queen would not commit them to burning, and she arranged to have the children put out to nurse, hoping that King Wivern would soften when he was back home again. The young Queen was given some food and some money, and told to go to the woods

So she went to the woods. She walked for one day, for two days, and was most miserable. Then she came to a great mountain, and she went up in silence. On the top of the mountain there were three seats and she sat down on the middle one. She was now distended with milk, because the two children had been taken away from her; so she sat down and milked herself.

Then two big birds flew up and alighted on either side of her, a swan and a crane. They pressed so close to her that her milk fell into their beaks. As she sat there, they changed suddenly into the most handsome Princes ever seen. The mountain became the most beautiful of royal castles, with servants, and stock, and gold and silver, and everything needful. The two Princes told her that a spell had been cast over them, from which they would never be freed until they had drunk the milk of a Queen who had first given birth to two boys. After that, she stayed with them, King Swan and King Crane; one would have her, and the other also, for she had saved them both.

When King Wivern reached home, he asked about his wife.

"You may well ask about her," said the old Queen. "A nice fellow you are! You did not give it a thought that she had saved you from great misery, since you could write that we were to burn both her and the children. Shame on you!"

"No! You wrote to tell me she had borne a puppy, and I wrote back that you were to let live what she had borne until my return."

They quarrelled about it for a long time. But at last they understood that the Red Knight had twisted their words. He was arrested, and had to confess what he had done. Then he was put into a spiked barrel, four horses were harnessed to it, and off they ran with it over marsh and bog.

But King Wivern was terribly grieved over his wife and his two children, now that he heard she had borne two lovely boys.

"You need not be anxious about the children," said the old Queen. "They were put out to nurse, and they are safe. But how she is getting on, I don't know. She was given some money and some food, and told to go the woods, and since then we have heard nothing of her."

King Wivern gave orders for the children to be brought home, and then he took some food and some money, and went to the woods to find his wife. He walked for two days, for three days, searching for her, but found nobody. At length he came to the castle in the wood. There he asked whether they had seen a strange maiden walking in the wood.

No, they had seen no one.

He went in to see what royalty lived in that castle, and as soon as he entered, he saw her. She saw him too, but she was frightened and fled, for she thought he was searching for her in order to have her burnt.

The two Princes came in and talked to him. They made friends, and he was asked to stay to dinner. He said he thought they had a lovely maiden there; what had become of her?

She had been so good, they said, she had saved them both. He asked from what evil she had saved them, and they told him all that had happened. Then he said that he, too, had a liking for her. Couldn't they make an agreement? They were to put some salt in their meal, and then she was to have the one whom she asked to drink to her. They were quite satisfied with that, for it could be decided at the same time which of them was to have her. They did not think she would ask the stranger to drink to her.

They went in to dinner, and she said:

"I think the food is very salty.

King Swan sits near to me,
King Crane is dear to me,
King Wivern will drink to me."

At once he took the silver jug and drank to her, and afterwards to the others. They had to do likewise, to drink his health and hers, even though they were discontented. Then he told them how she had saved him before she had saved them, so he thought he must be nearest to her.

He could have told them that before, they answered, then of course he would have had her. But he was not so sure.

He took her home, and the children had come home too. The castle in the wood was left to King Swan, who had a Princess from another kingdom. King Crane went to a third kingdom and got married. King Wivern and his Queen lived in happiness and glory all their lifetime, and they had more children. When last I was there, I had a tin sandwich on a wheat plate.


## ANN GEJ AND VISIVEJ

Once upon a time there was a witch. She lived in a castle, and she had a daughter named Ann Gej, who was not allowed to mix with Christian people until she was re-christened.

Not far from the castle lived a lad. He thought he would try what it was like to serve there. He went to the witch and asked her if she would have him as a groom. She asked his name, and he answered that he was called Visivej.

"Ann Gej and Visivej, the names go well together," said the witch, and she took him into her service.

Visivej looked after the horses for some time. Every time Ann Gej went out riding, he helped her on to the horse, and it was not long before the two were lovers. One day, Ann Gej hinted to Visivej that they might run away together. He readily agreed, but he didn't know how to escape the witch's power. Ann Gej answered that her mother would have no power over them if only they could avoid her for three days. So they agreed to run away next morning.

The next day came. The witch waited long for her daughter, but at last she lost patience. She searched the house, but Ann Gej was nowhere to be found. Then she sent a maid to the stables to look for Visivej,

70

but he, too, was gone. Then the witch knew, and she ordered twelve men to mount their twelve horses and ride along the road. Anything new or strange that they met with, they were to bring back.

When Ann Gej caught sight of the pursuers, she told Visivej her mother's men were after them, and she asked him what he thought they should do. Visivej didn't know.

"Will you be faithful to me, faithful until death?" asked Ann Gej.

"I will," said Visivej.

Then she turned Visivej into a brier and herself into a red rose on it. When the horsemen came to that place, some of them took a fancy to the red rose, but the others told them not to waste time on tomfoolery; they had better attend to their business. So they rode on, but when dusk was falling, they had to return without having performed their task. When they came to the witch, she asked them whether they had met with anything unusual on their way. They answered that they had come across nothing but a brier with a rose on it, but that was such a trifle that they would not waste any time taking it with them. The witch was annoyed and said:

"You ought to have taken the rose, and the brier would surely have come with it."

Next day she again sent out twelve horsemen in search of her daughter. When they were close on the heels of the fugitives, Ann Gej said to Visivej:

"Now my mother's men are coming, what are we to do now?"

Visivej was no wiser than last time.

"Will you be faithful to me, faithful until death?" asked Ann Gej.

"I will," answered Visivej.

Then she changed him into a church, and herself into a priest who stood preaching in the pulpit. When the horsemen arrived at the church, they thought it would be a good idea to hear a sermon, so they went in. After the service was ended, they mounted their horses and rode on, but had no better success than on the previous day. Towards evening, they returned to the castle. The witch asked them whether they had met with anything new. They answered that they had come across nothing but a church that had never been seen before; a priest had been preaching there, and they had entered the church to listen to him.

"Oh," said the witch, "you ought to have taken the priest, and the church would have been sure to come with him."

On the third day the witch rode out herself at the head of the twelve servants, and she took a golden apple with her. Now, she thought, it would be impossible for her daugther to escape her. When she had almost caught up with the two lovers, Ann Gej turned round and saw her.

"Now the fat is in the fire, if ever it was," said Ann Gej. "Now my mother is after us, whatever shall we do, Visivej?"

Visivej knew no way, however much he pondered and racked his brains.

"Will you be faithful to me, faithful until death?" she asked.

"I will," he replied.

"Then you must promise me not to take anything when my mother tries to entice you," she said.

He promised he would not. Thereupon she formed a lake, changed him into a drake, and herself into a duck. When the witch arrived, they were both swimming on the lake.

"Duckie, duckie, dilly-duck!" said the witch. It was part of her nature that she couldn't stand water, so she had to lure them. But however much she cried "Duckie, duckie, dilly-duck!" it was all in vain. Then she took her golden apple out of her pocket and held it over the water. The drake came swimming up and caught it in his beak. But as soon as she saw that, the duck darted up to him and knocked the golden apple out of his beak, and it sank to the bottom of the lake.

"Shame on you," said the witch, "that you make yourself wiser than me!"

The three days were now at an end. The witch no longer had any power over them, and they continued their journey with easy minds. When they had walked some distance, they came to an inn. The innkeeper was also a miller, who owned both a windmill and a watermill. He was well married and well-to-do. But what was the use? He had no children to inherit his riches.

Visivej was thirsty, and he said to Ann Gej that he had a mind to go in and have a glass of beer.

"You can go if you like," she said, "but don't be too long."

He went in and had his beer. Now there was a very pretty girl serving in the inn, whose name was Maren Scullery-maid. Visivej caught sight of her just as he was about to leave, and no sooner had he seen her than he clean forgot Ann Gej and all his former life. The two became lovers. Presently the innkeeper came in, and Visivej asked him whether he was not in need of a miller's hand. He couldn't exactly say he was, but as Visivej looked a good sort, he thought he might as well keep him. And Visivej stayed there.

Ann Gej waited for him a long time, but her waiting was in vain.

So she turned herself into a duck and swam through the gutter into the scullery, and flew up on to the copper. There she transformed herself into a gilt pin with a gilt head. When Maren went to take the lid off the copper, she saw the gilt pin. She took it to her mistress and asked leave to keep it.

"Indeed you may," said the mistress. "It must have been dropped by one of the visitors, and you can have it."

When Sunday came, Maren Scullery-maid went again to her mistress and asked permission to go to church.

"To be sure you may," said she, "but I know quite well why you want to go to church. It's because you want to show off the gilt pin."

Maren went to her room and opened the chest, expecting to find the pin where she had left it. But there was no pin to be found. But in the chest there lay a baby, crying for all it was worth. When she saw that, Maren was very frightened; however, she took courage, put the baby on her arm, and took it to the innkeeper's wife. She told her mistress how she had found the child, and asked her advice as to what to do with it. The innkeeper's wife said she would take the baby herself and adopt it as her own daughter. Then she told the maid to rush up to the mill and tell her husband that he had had a daughter that day. No sooner did the miller hear the news than he ran down to the house. Now at last his greatest wish, to have a child to inherit his property, was fulfilled.

At the mill there was great rejoicing in little Ann Gej. It was not many months before she could walk, and soon she could also knit and sew. When she was two years of age, she was full grown, and there was not her equal in all the perfections and accomplishments of a woman. When she was quite grown-up, her father built a cottage for her on a hill; and he gave her a pair of pigeons and a red calf.

Now at that time, it was the custom to give all the servants linen, and the innkeeper's three hands had their linen all right. They were to have shirts made from it. They wanted these shirts to be well made, and they thought they would prefer the maiden to make them; but none of them had the courage to ask her to do so. At last, the lowest of the miller's hands thought he could but try. He went up the hill, taking the linen with him, and begged the little maiden earnestly to do him a favour and sew him a shirt. She answered that, to be sure, she would do that for him. He could come again for the shirt on the following evening. But he had better have his supper before he came, for there might still be some stitches to be added when he arrived, and she couldn't offer him any food. Well, next day, when he had had his supper, he went up the hill and entered the cottage.

"Good evening!" said he.

"Thank you," said she.

"Is the shirt ready?" he asked.

"The buttonhole is still lacking," she said. "Please sit down while I do it."

When the shirt was quite finished, she gave it to him. He thanked her and asked how much he owed her. She said she would not take anything, since he was in her father's service.

"You could, however, do me a favour," she said.

He answered that he would willingly do her any service that was within his power. Then she asked him to stay with her for the night, for she was lonely and lacked company.

To be sure he would. When they had been together for some time, she said:

"Oh, how bad! There is something I have forgotten to do."

The lad asked if he couldn't do it for her.

"I am sure you can," she said, "if you will do me that service too. After all, it is nothing but that I have forgotten to stir my fire. When you are in the kitchen and have taken hold of the poker, you can tell me; then I'll tell you how the rest should be done."

He went to the kitchen, took hold of the poker, and called out:

"Now I have it!"

"You hold the poker," she said, "the poker is sure to hold you till the morning."

So the lad had to keep standing there; he could neither twist nor turn until daybreak. Then the maiden released him.

The other hands saw the shirt, and each of them thought to himself:

"If the lowest servant can get the maiden to sew him a shirt, I think I can make her do it as well."

In this confident assurance, the second of the miller's hands went up to the house on the hill, taking his linen.

"Good evening!" said he.

"Thank you," said she.

He then asked the maiden if she would do him the favour to make him a shirt. To be sure she would. He was to come again next day when he had had his supper; there might still be some stitches to be added when he arrived, and she couldn't offer him anything to eat. Well satisfied with her answer, he returned home, and didn't forget to do as he had been told. Next day, as soon as he had had his supper, he went to the house on the hill. He asked her whether the shirt was ready, and she answered there was still a buttonhole to be stitched, and she must ask him to wait just a moment. When she had put in the last stitch, she gave him the shirt. He thanked her and asked what he owed her for her trouble. She answered that she would take nothing, since he was in her father's service, but if he would do her a little favour, she would be very glad.

He enquired what sort of service he could do her, and was told that she would ask him to stay with her for the night, since she lived in such a lonely place and missed company. Well, he would willingly comply with her wish, to be sure. When they had been sitting for some time together, the maiden said that, oh how bad! there was something she had forgotten to do. The lad asked her what it was.

"I have forgotten to bolt the door," she answered.

"Certainly I'll do it for you," said he.

"Thank you," she said, "tell me when you have put your hand on the bolt, and I'll let you know what to do next."

He went out, seized the bolt, and called out: "I hold it now!"

When she heard that, she said:

"You hold the bolt, the bolt is sure to hold you till morning."

Now the poor fellow was forced to stand there in the cold all through the long and frosty night until daybreak. Then the maiden released him.

He returned to the inn with the shirt. He showed it to Visivej, and told him that the maiden on the hill had sewn it for him. Visivej, hearing this, thought he could easily get the maiden to sew him a shirt also, since he was the best hand. As soon as dusk had fallen, he took his linen and went up the hill with it. He stepped into the maiden's house and, greeting her, he asked, as the others had done, if she would make him a shirt. He told her that he was soon to marry Maren Scullery-maid. He said he was very fond of dancing, and when he danced, he would like to undo his coat. So he would ask her to embroider the shirt beautifully over the breast, because that would look very nice.

She promised to do as she was asked, and told him to come again next day when he had had his supper. He went home, and next day, after having his supper, he again made for the house on the hill.

"Good evening!" said he.

"Thank you," said she, "and welcome!"

These last words she hadn't said to any of the others, for she knew well that he was Visivej; but he was unaware that she was Ann Gej.

He then asked if the shirt was ready. She answered that there was still a buttonhole to be stitched, and asked him to wait until it had been done. When the shirt was quite finished, and Visivej had received it, he thanked her and asked how much he owed for her trouble. She replied that she would take nothing, since he was in her father's service. However, he could do her a favour in return, if he was willing.

Well, he would readily do her any service, if only it was within his power to fulfill her wish.

She then asked him to stay with her for the night; but he answered that it would really be hard for him to comply with her request, for he was to marry Maren Scullery-maid next day, and there were some preparations to be made. He asked her to excuse him, for really he had no time to spare. But he would be delighted if the maiden could come tomorrow and see their play and merriment.

She thanked him for that, but indeed, it was so tiresome for her to be all alone, and now that she had done him the service of sewing and embroidering a shirt, it was only fair that he should do her the service of staying the night.

Well, yes, if it must be, it should be so, and he agreed to stay.

When they had been sitting together for a while, the maiden said:

"Oh, how bad! There is a thing I have forgotten to do."

Visivej asked her what that was.

"I have forgotten to take the red calf into the shed. Now he stands brawling out there, and we'll have no peace for him until he gets in."

Visivej said he would willingly lead the calf in, but he wanted first to be told how to do it. The maiden answered that he must seize the calf by the tail, and tell her when that had been done. Then she would let him know how to cope with the rest. So he went out, took hold of the calf's tail, and called: "I hold him now!"

"Well, now you hold the tail, the tail is sure to hold you until the morning," said the maiden; and she said to the calf: "Run with him over hill and mountain and deep dales!"

Off went the calf, running, as the maiden had said, over hill and mountain and deep dales, all the night long until dawn. Then he stopped before her door. The maiden released Visivej, and he returned, scratched and bleeding, to the inn, where his wounds were dressed.

The innkeeper took out his best carriage and harnessed his best pair of horses to it. The bride and the bridegroom got in, and now it was time to set off for the church. But when one horse went forward, the other went backwards. No good driving could come of that! Another pair of horses were put in, but in vain; when one horse went forward, the other went backwards. They tried with a third pair of horses, but with no better success. Then Visivej remembered the maiden's strong calf. A messenger was sent up the hill to ask if she would lend them the red calf to draw them to church.

Yes, she would readily give him that pleasure.

The red calf was harnessed to the carriage. He drew them to the church with no effort at all, and back to the inn again when the wedding was over. There was feasting and drinking, as is customary on such occasions. When it was over, the maiden came. She sat down all by herself in an out-of-the-way room. Visivej went in and asked her if she wouldn't like to amuse herself with a dance. She said she wouldn't, but asked him to stay a little while with her, since she was so alone, sitting there.

Well, if it would please her, certainly he would do her that service.

The pair of pigeons that her father had given her used to go with her everywhere. She had brought a little casket; now she opened it, and took out a barley-corn. The male pigeon at once snatched it, but the hen came hurrying up and knocked it out of his beak.

"That is what Ann Gej did to Visivej when he caught the golden apple," said the maiden.

"What are you saying?" asked Visivej and he begged her: "Do it again!"

She said she hadn't many corns to squander, but since he desired it so keenly, she would humour him. She took out a barley-corn, and it was snatched by the male pigeon, but the hen knocked it off his beak.

"That is what Ann Gej did to Visivej when he snatched the golden apple," she said.

"Are you Ann Gej?" he asked.

"I am," she said.

Then Visivej recovered his memory. He went to the innkeeper and told him how it had all come about. A priest was called in. Ann Gej was re-christened, and Visivej was married once more, and to her. This time, then, Maren Scullery-maid was not provided for.

The old witch died, and they inherited all her riches. They also inherited the inn, and both mills as well. There they are still settled and living happily to this very day.

## IN THE HILLMAN'S SERVICE

There was a man who had three sons. They were, of course, called Povl, Per, and Esben Ashrake. He was called so by his brothers because he was always indoors with his mother, and there he lay by the hearth, raking the ashes. When they were all three grown-up, their father said to them one day:

"Look here, lads! Now you must go out into the world and support yourselves. I cannot afford to have you hanging about at home any longer."

Well, Povl was ready to go at once. He packed his knapsack and went off. It was not long before he met a little man in grey clothes, with a red cap on his head.

"Hullo, my son," said the old man, "where are you off to?"

"I am out to try and find a place," answered Povl.

"That comes in pat, for I have come out to hire a farmhand. If you will serve me, I'll give you a bushel of money when the year is over. You'll have to do everything I ask of you, and he who is the first to get angry will have a slice cut out of his belly, and a slice out of his backside. Will you consent to that agreement, my son?"

Povl said he would. He thought he would have a whole bushel of money when the year was over, and he had never seen as much as that before. So he went home with the hillman. Now it was evening.

"Can you go and rock the child, little Povl?" said the hillman.

So Povl sat rocking the cradle while the hillwoman ladled out the supper and put it on the table before her husband and herself, leaving Povl by the cradle. He stole a wistful glance at the porringer, but nobody cared. When they had finished their meal, the hillman said:

"Now you had better go to bed, so as to be up early tomorrow and do some work."

He then showed him where to lie down, and it was not long before Povl fell asleep.

Next morning the hillman said to him:

"Time for you to get up, Povl. First you must clean the stable and groom the horses, and then go ploughing. You can plough, can't you?"

Well, he could, to be sure.

"That's a good thing, for I need some ploughing done. But I suppose you haven't got a watch to go by?"

No, Povl had no watch.

"It doesn't matter," said the hillman, "for I have a dog here. He can go with you; he is sure to lie down at the end of the field, and when he goes home, you can come too."

Certainly Povl would do all this; and with these instructions he went off. The dog lay down at the end of the field, and stayed there, very comfortably. When it was noon, all the people in the neighbouring fields went home. But the dog did not budge.

"Confound that damned dog!" thought Povl. He was almost starving, for he had had nothing to eat since he left home. However, he went on ploughing until evening; and then, at last, the dog went home.

So Povl went back to the hillman's house at last also, but his patience was at an end. As soon as he was in the courtyard, he tore the harness off the horses and hurled it, clinking, along the paving. The hillman came out.

"What's up? You seem to be throwing the harness away very fast. You are not angry, are you?"

"Well, I scarcely know what to say to that," said Povl. "I have been here since yesterday, and never a bite to eat have I had. I don't call that decent!"

"I see. You are not satisfied with my service? Well, then, you know what has been agreed between us," said the hillman. "Now I'll cut a slice from your belly and a slice from your backside."

When he had done so, Povl was allowed to go where he liked. At length, he came dragging himself home to his father, and there was much lamentation when they heard what had happened to him.

Now it was Per who must go out to service, for the father could not support them all. He advised him to try to come out better than his brother. But, to cut a long story short, he had no better luck. He met the hillman, was engaged, and of course, he was the first to get angry, whereupon he suffered the same treatment as Povl. Things looked bad for his father when he, too, returned. Now both strapping fellows were lying at home, and neither could work at all.

"Now I think I had better be off," said Esben, "to see whether I shall have the same bad luck as my big brothers."

"Yes, indeed," said the father. "Since they have not been able to make shift for themselves, I am afraid things will go utterly wrong with you. But do at all costs be careful not to enter the hillman's service!"

"Ho-ho! He is the very man I want to go to," said Esben. "It must be great fun to serve a hillman!"

Then he packed his clothes, put spoon and fork and knife in his pocket, and went off.

It was not long before he met the hillman, and he at once took service with him on the same terms as Povl and Per, and went with him to his home. It was just evening when they arrived. Then the hillman said:

"Can you rock the child while your mistress ladles out the supper?"

Well, certainly he could.

The hillwoman ladled out a very good ale-caudle for supper, but not the slightest hint was given that Esben should join them. He was, how-ever, equal to the occasion. He left the cradle, went calmly up to the table, and sat down in their company. Then he took his spoon out of his pocket and began to eat. It is true they scowled at him a little, but that was no business of his. He ate a good supper, for he liked the food quite well, and when he had finished eating, he put the spoon back into his pocket. Then the hillman showed him his bed, and Esben slept well until morning.

When morning came, the hillman said:

"Well, little Esben, now you must get up to clean the stable and groom the horses."

Esben finished that job in a hurry, and went in to see if breakfast was ready. And sure enough, at the very same moment, the hillwoman came in with a fine bacon omelette and put it on the table. Esben went calmly up, sat down at the table, took knife and fork from his pocket, and began to eat. They glanced at him, it is true, but he did not care. When he had finished eating, he put knife and fork back into his pocket.

"Well, little Esben, can you now go out to plough?"

Certainly he could.

"You see, I need to have some ploughing done. But I suppose you have not got a watch?"

No, he had no watch.

"It does not matter, anyhow," said the hillman. "Here is a dog to take with you. When he goes home, you can come too."

The dog lay at the end of the field and stayed there. At noon all the neighbours went home, but the dog didn't budge.

"To hell with that dog!" thought Esben. He snatched up one of the plough-handles and hit the dog a hard blow on his side. Howling and yelling, the dog ran homewards for all he was worth. Now Esben got busy. He took out his pocket-knife and cut all the four traces; then he leapt on one of the horses, and rode off homewards after the dog.

No sooner had he come into the courtyard than the hillman came out.

"Why have you come rushing home, little Esben? What's up?"

"I'll tell you, master," said Esben. "I don't know what possessed that damned dog. All of a sudden, he began to howl and yell, and then ran homewards as if he were in a bad way, and I had to cut the traces. Otherwise I was afraid you would be angry when the dog arrived, and I had not come with him."

"I have been little short of duped," said the hillman.

"You are not angry, master, are you?" said Esben.

No, oh no, that was out of the question.

Some time passed. Esben attended to his duties. Then one day, the hillman said:

"Look here, Esben, can you look after my pigs in the wood?"

Well, to be sure, Esben could do that.

"I must tell you that in the autumn I usually drive my pigs to the wood when the beechmast and acorns are ripe, and let them fatten there."

On the first day, he himself took Esben out to the woods.

"Now you may let them run about the wood," he said, "but over there you see a big miry hole. Take care that they don't run into it. Otherwise we shall not be able to get them out again."

Yes, Esben would take care, to be sure. The hillman went home.

Esben walked about the woods for a long time, looking after the pigs. The hillman was well satisfied with him, for now the pigs were nearly fat enough. But one day, Esben took out his pocket-knife, cut off all the pigs' tails, and stuck their thick ends in the mire. Then he drove all the pigs home to his father, who was very glad of all the good pork. This done, Esben ran back to the hillman's house and cried out:

"Things have gone all wrong, master, for all the pigs have run into the mire, and there is nothing to be seen of them but the tails!"

When the hillman heard that, he ran at once towards the wood, and Esben after him. He hurried to the hole and began to tug at one of the tails in order to pull out the pig, but the tail broke, and the hillman fell backwards into the mire. Esben now hastened to the spot to help him pull out the pigs, but it was the same thing with all of them.

"I thought as much," said the hillman, "they were too fat. Now the tails won't hold in pulling them out. I have been little short of duped!"

"You are not angry, master, are you?" said Esben.

No, oh no, he was not at all angry.

After some time, the hillman said: "I say, little Esben, can you drive to the mill today? We need some corn ground for Christmas."

Well, Esben could do so, to be sure.

The hillman measured off the corn himself and carried it out to the cart.

8

"Listen now, little Esben, you must try to make them grind it as fine as sand, for they are somewhat lazy with their grinding."

"I'll do so, master, to be sure," said Esben, and he drove off. But he did not go to the mill. Instead, he drove home to his father with the corn. Then he drove to a sandpit that was owned by his father, where there was good fine sand. He filled the bags with sand and took them home to the hillman.

When the hillwoman was about to bake, of course she discovered that the bags were full of sand instead of flour, and she told her husband.

"How is this, little Esben?" said he.

"Why, didn't you tell me to ask them to grind it as fine as sand? And so I did."

"I have been little short of duped," said the hillman.

"You are not angry, master, are you?" said Esben.

Oh no, certainly, not in the least.

Again some time passed. One day, the hillman said:

"I am going to town today, and you'll have to help your mistress at home; for she is very busy today."

Well, Esben would do so, to be sure, and the hillman drove away. The woman was brewing beer, and Esben had to carry in water and peat for her. Suddenly she said:

"Look here, little Esben, can you go and see if the child is awake, and if he has dirtied himself? If so, you must clean him both outside and in. Can you do this, little Esben?"

"Yes, to be sure," said Esben, and he went in to the child. Sure enough, the child was awake and had dirtied himself. Esben took him to the brook, stripped him to the skin, washed and scrubbed both the boy and his clothes in the brook, and hung them up on the fencepickets. Then he went quietly into the room and sat down. Presently the hillwoman came in and said:

"Dear me, Esben! Where have you left the child?"

"Well, you see, he had dirtied himself, and I have cleaned him both outside and in, as you asked me to do, and I have hung both the boy and his clothes on the fence to dry."

"Dear me!" cried the woman, "the child must have frozen to death!"

And out she ran to see the poor child. But he was both stiff and dead, and no wonder, for it was very cold. Here was a nice mess; but nothing could be done about it any more.

At noon the hillman returned and asked for something to eat.

"But where is the child, my dear wife?" he asked. "I can't see him."

She told him what Esben had done with the child, and how she had found him frozen quite stiff when she went out to him.

"That's too bad!" said the hillman. "I have been little short of duped!"

"You are not angry, master, are you?" said Esben, who stood listening to them.

No, oh no, he could not think of such a thing.

Some days passed. Then the hillman said to Esben:

"Today we are going to a feast, my wife and I. Meantime, you can trim the midden a little; and when you have finished that, you can try to arrange something safe down by the brook, for my crossing tonight; for I expect it will be dark before I return, and maybe I shall be a little tipsy, and not quite steady on my legs. When you have done that, you can come to the place where the feast is held, and have a dance and amuse yourself in the evening as long as we are there. And you can cast a good eye at me now and then; that will please me. And it would be a good thing if you can arrange for some light to see by when we are returning home. Let me see, little Esben, that you do as I have told you."

"To be sure I will, master," said Esben.

The hillman and his wife went to the feast. And you can bet that Esben then got busy. First he swept the courtyard, and then he hauled all their furniture and possessions on to the midden and piled it up there: chests and cupboards, tables and chairs, pots and saucepans, and frying-pans as well.

"There! That's well done!" he thought to himself, "but what can I find to put across the brook?"

Then he bethought himself that he would take four of their best cows. He drove them down to the water, killed them, and laid them in the brook with the horns upwards, so that there were four horns on either side, like a hand-rail. There now! That was well done! But he still had to find some very good eyes to cast at the hillman. It struck him that they had four good sheep; their eyes were certainly good, and they could be used. He seized the sheep, killed them, and took out their eyes.

"There now! That is that!" said Esben. "Now I am ready to go to the feast, and indeed, it will soon be getting dark. Come to think of it, I was to arrange for some light. Of course, I could bring the lantern, yet I think that will not be necessary, for if I set the barn on fire now, I am sure we can find our way by the light."

He then put on his best clothes, and before leaving, he set fire to the barn.

Now everything was as it should be. He went to the feast. There he was kindly welcomed, given both food and drink, and then invited to come to the parlour for a dance. The hillman was there too, and every time he glanced at Esben, the lad managed to throw one of the sheep's eyes at his head. The hillman did not like that much, and of course, he wondered what those wet lumps were that Esben threw at his head every time he glanced at him.

So it was not long before the hillman went to his wife and said they must be going home now. But she was for staying a little longer. She pleaded that Esben had only just arrived, and why shouldn't he, too, have some merriment? But her words were lost on the hillman, and they went away at once. When they were outside, he said:

"Now I come to think of it, little Esben, did you bring the lantern?"

"No, master, you only told me to arrange for a light, so I set the barn on fire before leaving. I thought it would be possible for us to find our way by that. You can see for yourself how brightly and clearly it is burning."

"I have been little short of duped," said the hillman.

"You are not angry, master, are you?" said Esben.

No, oh no, he was not at all angry.

"But tell me, little Esben, what were those lumps you threw at my head while you were dancing?"

"Indeed I'll tell you that, master. You told me to throw some really good eyes at you when I was up there, and I could think of nothing better than to put out the eyes of our four best sheep, for I am sure they must have good eyes, and it was those I threw at you, master."

"I have been little short of duped," said the hillman.

"You are not angry, master, are you?" said Esben.

No, oh no, he could not think of such a thing.

A little later, they arrived at the brook. The hillman led the way, and he said:

"I wonder what it is that you have put into the brook, little Esben? It seems to be yielding and ever yielding under me."

"Indeed I'll tell you that, master. You told me to put something really safe into the brook for crossing, and I could think of nothing better than to take our four best cows and kill them, and so I took them and laid them here. Now you can see for yourself. At either side there are four horns that you can lean on."

"I have been little short of duped," said the hillman.

"You are not angry, master, are you?"

No, oh no, not at all.

84

At length they reached home, and the hillman went quite calmly up to the barn and blew out the fire as if it had been a candle.

"But what are all those things on top of the midden, little Esben?" he asked, when he caught sight of all that had been piled up there.

"I'll tell you that, master. You told me to have the courtyard swept and the midden trimmed, and I could think of nothing but to take all our furniture and things to put on it, and that was not at all easy. You bet I have been busy all day."

"I have been little short of duped," said the hillman.

"You are not angry, master, are you?"

No, oh no, that was out of the question.

Esben then had to help the hillman take some of the things into the house again, and when they had finished that, they went to bed. Esben had his bed in the kitchen, and there was only a thin wall between it and the bed in which the hillman slept. So he could lie there and hear what the hillman said to his wife. That night, the hillman was in anything but a good temper when he got to bed.

"It will be false reckoning, my dear wife, if we keep that Esben. He spoils everything for us. Whatever am I to do to get rid of him?"

The hillwoman did not know. It must be for himself to think something out.

"I think there will be no remedy but to kill him, and I may as well do it tonight. I expect he is sleeping fast after the feast."

But Esben heard these words, you see. And what was he to do? He jumped out of bed and took hold of a big club from the kitchen, and he put it on his pillow. Then he took a big pot with some water in it, and put that under the eiderdown. As for himself, he crawled under the bed.

Before long, the hillman came creeping in with a big axe. He listened, as you may suppose, to make sure that everything was still and silent. Then, swinging the axe with all his might, he hit the club. There was a terrible noise. That seemed to be all right, but he thought he had better strike a blow on the belly as well; and there was a terrible splash.

"Well," thought the hillman, "now I think he is done for!" Thereupon he went quietly to his bed and lay down.

After a while, Esben could hear him snore. He crawled out from under the bed, gathered the club and the potsherds together, and then went to bed himself. He slept peacefully until daybreak.

When he came in for breakfast, the hillman stared, I can tell you!

"Look here!" he said to the hillwoman. "Can't you give me clean sheets and a shirt, mistress? Last night I was bitten by a flea, and when I killed it, both the bed and I got dirty."

Then without more ado he went out to his work.

"There you are!" said the hillman to his wife. "He counts that blow as no more than a flea-bite! I don't know how it is all going to end. There is nothing for it but to offer him money for leaving, since there is no other remedy."

She answered that that was for himself to decide.

A little later Esben came in, and the hillman said to him:

"Look here, little Esben, do you know what I have been thinking?"

No, he did not know that, to be sure.

"You see, I have bethought myself that I don't need a farmhand any longer. I think I can do the work myself. So I would like you to leave now, and I will pay you your wages for the whole year."

"Well, I would willingly do so," said Esben, "but I dare not do it because of my father. When I go home and say I have had to leave service before my time, I am afraid he will kill me."

"But surely he won't be angry if I give you your wages for the whole year."

"It makes no difference, for I dare not do it," said Esben.

The hillman was at a loss to know how to get rid of Esben. He dared not offer him all the money he could carry, for he was afraid Esben could carry more than he had. Then it struck him that he might offer him all the money he could cart with a team of two horses.

"Now, listen to me, little Esben. If I give you all the money I can cart with a team of two horses, what would you say?"

"Well," said Esben, "you must cart the money home to my father's house yourself, and tell him I have served you truly and loyally, and that I am not leaving because you have got tired of me. If you'll agree to that, master, I'll agree too."

Well, the hillman consented to the arrangement, and he managed to scoop up the money on to the cart while Esben packed his clothes. Then they drove home to the lad's father. The hillman told him he must not be angry with Esben for coming home before his time; really, he had been quite satisfied with him. So saying, he went off.

I dare say Esben and his father smacked their lips when the hillman had gone! Now they had got compensation for what his brothers had had to suffer. And they lived in prosperity and happiness for many years on the money they had from the hillman.

# GERMANY

## HOW A SMITH MADE HIS FORTUNE

Once upon a time there was a blacksmith, a poor, simple man, who had two sons, one of whom was not very good at his work. The father said to the elder son:

"At the moment there isn't much work to do here; it would be a good idea for you to travel to another country, that is, if you'd like to. And make sure that you earn a good wage and get to know the business a little better!"

Jan was by nature a fine, smart and strapping fellow. He set out on his way. He met a good blacksmith and asked him for work, provided that he was paid a good wage. The smith agreed, and Jan worked for him for some time.

One day there was a notice in the newspaper, saying that the King's daughter wanted to be married but could not find a husband to suit her taste. The King was preparing a banquet for a certain day, and to this all the young men were invited. When Jan's master read this, he said to him:

"On such and such a day, the King wishes to invite all the young people to a banquet, to choose a husband for his daughter."

"There is no point in my going," said Jan. "She won't even look at me."

"That doesn't matter," said the smith. "That's nothing to stop you from going. You must scrub yourself till you are quite clean, and put on my best frock-coat. Then you'll be quite fit to go."

Jan was easily persuaded, and went to the feast. When all the young men had been in the castle for a little while, they were ushered into a magnificent hall. One by one they took their places for the banquet, and of course, a wonderful feast was spread before them. The aged King wandered round the tables with his daughter and her old mother; and the eyes of all the young men were fixed on the daughter. But it was Jan whom she seemed to like best. She whispered to the King that he must call him secretly into another room.

No sooner said than done. The King told Jan that it was he whom the Princess had chosen, and then he asked him what he did for a living, and who his parents were.

"Oh," said Jan, "I'm nothing but a poor blacksmith." And he told him the whole story of his life, where he lived, and where he was now employed. Then he was allowed to go, and went back to his master's house.

When some time had gone by, he was again ordered to come before the King.

"There you are," said his master. "The Princess' choice has fallen upon you, and you alone!"

"O, I think I know better than that," said Jan. "I'll take my tools with me; perhaps I am to shoe the horses."

When he arrived at the castle, the servants brought him before the King, who went with him and his daughter into another chamber, and the Queen followed them. Then the King explained that the Princess was not eager for riches, land, and noble birth. Character was all that mattered to her, and that was why she had chosen Jan. The young man was then asked to describe again where his parents lived, and what kind of people they were; and after that he was dismissed.

When he returned to his master's house, he said nothing about the Princess. He simply told the smith he had shod a few old nags, and then he got on with his work.

A few more weeks passed, and once again Jan was summoned to the castle. The servants led him straight into the presence of the King and the Princess, who told him that, as this was his second visit, they would like to announce the engagement without delay, and hold the wedding immediately afterwards. There was no need for him to go away again, and he could move into the castle without further ado.

The wedding festivities lasted for three days, and when they were over, Jan wrote home that he had been crowned King. At first his old parents could hardly believe it. But Jan was not very happy in his new life. So magnificent a way of living was quite new to him, and he began to feel a little homesick, though he was careful not to show it.

He told his wife he would like to visit his parents. She said he could do so if he really wanted to, but she would like to go with him. Jan thought about this for a while, and then said that as his parents were only simple people, he would prefer to go alone for this first time. In the end the King and the Princess let him do as he pleased. He set off in a carriage drawn by four white horses. He drove all day and when night began to fall, he went to a large inn and asked if he and his horses could be given shelter for the night.

"Of course!" said the landlord, "and there are plenty of stables."

Jan fed his horses, and then he went into the inn. There he found a whole crowd of young fellows who seemed to be rolling in wealth. They asked him to join them in a game of cards. He sat down at their table, but the young men were too clever for him, and soon he had gambled away his horses and all his possessions, down to the shirt off his back.

When he had lost everything, the innkeeper, out of the kindness of his heart, gave him a few old rags to wear, and Jan started out once more to visit his parents. When he drew near their house, his brother, Hinnerk, who was rather stupid, happened to look out of the smithy window, and saw him coming from afar. He could scarcely believe his eyes, and cried out:

"Father, I think that is our Jan coming back! He looks even more ragged than before – wasn't he the one who was going to be King?"

When Jan arrived and greeted his parents, they said to him: "Jan, we thought you were King!"

"Oh, well," he answered, "when one's bored and far away in a foreign country, one can write almost anything."

Next day he started work again in the smithy. A fortnight passed by, and the Princess began to be very anxious, since no message had come from her husband. But she knew where he lived, and so she set out in a splendid coach-and-pair, taking her coachman with her. She came to the inn where Jan had lodged, and when she saw the horses, and the harness hanging on the wall, she was seized with terror, thinking he had lost his life there. She asked the innkeeper how such a fine set of harness came to be in his yard, and he told her the whole story. Then she bought back all Jan's belongings and his clothing from the innkeeper and packed them into a fine case; and next morning she set off again on her journey.

When she was close to his parent's house, she told the coachman to wait for her at a nearby inn, as she was going to visit someone. She walked on towards the house, and Jan saw her coming from afar. He went hot and cold with excitement, but he said not a word. But at last Hinnerk also noticed that a fine lady was coming towards their home, and he cried: "Father! What is that lovely girl coming here for?"

The Princess came in and shook hands with the old people. She told them of her adventures on the way, and that she was Jan's wife. Poor Jan went scarlet with embarrassment, but she comforted him by saying that things were not really so bad. They were not short of money, and she had bought back all his possessions, so that the King need know nothing about it.

She spent the night in Jan's house and had to sleep by his side. In the early hours of the morning, Hinnerk yelled harshly: "Jan, it's high time you were out; into the smithy with you." Then he flung open the door and shouted:

"Good heavens! Father! Mother! Look! Our Jan is lying in bed with the beautiful girl!"

Jan heard that, and said to the Princess: "We had better get up quickly!"

"Jan will never have to work in the smithy any more," said the Princess. "You can all come home with us."

So they all went together to the royal castle, where another magnificent banquet was prepared for them. And there they lived happily ever after.

## THE PRINCESS IN THE UNDERWORLD

Once upon a time there lived a Princess, who was doomed by a curse to spend the rest of her days in a castle in the depths of the earth. The King had proclaimed that whoever could set his daughter free should have her hand in marriage.

Now, there were three young fellows, one of whom was supposed to be rather stupid. They strayed into a certain wood. They knew the Princess was in that wood, but they did not know how they could get into the castle. So they wandered round and round, looking for a way in.

Then they saw a rope hanging high up with a basket attached to it, and they hoisted themselves up the rope and let themselves down into the castle. When they got down below, they saw a table standing in a room. Beneath it a black dog was lying, a very large one. On the table lay a gun, and beside it was a note which read: "Any one who lifts this gun has power over all things."

So they lifted it, and a white horse came galloping up and asked them what they desired. They said they had come to rescue the King's daughter.

Then the white horse came, bringing the Princess with him. The two fellows went away with her, leaving the stupid boy behind. But they had forgotten the Princess' crown. However, the stupid one had seen the crown and picked it up.

When they were above ground, the two boys said:

"Now, as the other isn't with us, we'll let go the rope when the basket is in the middle, and he will fall down dead."

The stupid one heard what they were saying, and thought:

"I'll show you!"

He then went away and filled the basket half-full of stones. The others up there said:

"Now, here he comes!"

So they let go the rope, and thought: "Now he is surely dead."

However, he stood there and could not get out of the castle again. The others went off rejoicing with the King's daughter. Then he picked up the gun once more. Thereupon the white horse returned and asked him what he desired. Of course, he wanted to escape from the castle. He had tried again and again, but all in vain. So the white horse told him to wait until midnight, and then he would carry him out.

He said to him: "Just you sit on my back, and I will carry you to safety."

When he reached the open air again, the others were not to be seen. He made his own way after them, taking the crown with him. When he came to the town, he went to the goldsmith who made crowns in his workshop, and asked if there was any work for him.

"What can you do?" asked the smith.

"Well," he answered, "I can make crowns."

"Then you are just the man I need," said the smith. "You must make a crown for the Princess who is to be married, now that she has been rescued from the castle."

He was sent straight away into a room, where he was quite alone, and a meal was brought in for him. The smith wished to know how much time he would need for his work.

"Oh, just three days," he replied.

On the first day he placed a few parts of the crown on the table because he noticed that his master was watching him closely. The smith had become suspicious, and was peeping through the keyhole.

On the second day, he put almost half of it on the table, and on the third day he had it all ready at the arranged time. Then his master told him to accompany him and bring the crown along with him. He must try it out, to see if it fitted.

They came to the royal palace. The Princess, sitting in the window, was watching them. She asked them to come before her. When they entered her room, she threw her arms round the lad's neck and cried:

"Here is the one who saved me!"

The others were sent away, and he was given the Princess' hand in marriage.

# AUSTRIA

## ONCE IN, NEVER OUT AGAIN

Once upon a time there was a father who had three sons called Hans, Sepp, and Jörg. As they were all grown up, he sent them on their travels, to seek their fortunes. Before they went, he gave each of them a knife and told them to travel together until they came to a certain lime-tree where three ways branched off. Each was to bury his knife near the lime-tree in the direction in which he intended to continue his travels. If one of them came back, he was to look and see if his brothers' knives were still untarnished. Should one of them be rusty, he was to hurry to the help of that brother, because the rust was a sign that misfortune had overtaken him. The sons promised to follow their father's advice in every way and took their leave of him.

The three young men set out, and soon they came to the lime-tree of which their father had told them. Each one buried his knife. Then they bade each other farewell, and went on their separate ways.

Hans went straight on. After a time, he came to an inn and decided to rest there for a while. He began to talk with the innkeeper, and when he was ready to go again, the innkeeper gave him a tame lion, and told him he would be able to make good use of it.

Presently Hans came to a town. Here he saw that everybody was very unhappy, and that black flags hung from all the windows. Feeling very curious, he went into the first inn he came to, ordered something to eat and drink, and when he had satisfied his hunger, he asked the landlord why everyone was so sad. The landlord told him that a dragon lived in a gorge nearby, and had the whole town in his power. The safety of the people depended on this monster, and in order to prevent him from ravaging the town, a maiden had to be given to him several times a year. Now all the maidens had already been delivered to him, and the only one left was the King's daughter. She was to be taken to the gorge and given to the dragon next day, and that was why the town was in such deep mourning. No one dared to challenge the monster.

Hans offered to kill the dragon, and asked to be brought before the King. The innkeeper, who held an office at the King's court, was eager to help him, and without more ado, the two of them set off for the palace. When they arrived, they were promptly given an audience, and Hans again offered to kill the dragon; but for this task he demanded a good sword.

The King agreed joyfully and promised to give Hans the Princess' hand in marriage, should he succeed in killing the monster. So Hans was given a trusty sword, and he and the innkeeper went back to the inn.

On the following day, the Princess was taken to the gorge, to be sacrificed to the dragon. As it was still possible that Hans might lose the fight, she was driven there in a jet-black coach. The townspeople were full of sorrow, yet they were also full of hope that at last the dragon might be killed, and the town freed from its oppressor.

Hans girded on his sword and called his lion, and thus protected, he went down to the gorge. He had not gone far before he heard the monster's snorts, and before very long the creature came into view.

When the dragon saw a man in front of him instead of a maiden, he flew into a furious rage; his snorts grew even more terrible, and he charged down on Hans as fast as he could. But Hans came on too, the sword in his hand and the lion by his side. Then the fight began. Hans kept calm and skilfully managed to avoid all the dragon's attacks. When the monster was once again bearing down upon him, he quickly sprang to one side, so that the dragon rushed past him and came to a halt right in front of him. Then Hans plunged his sword into the dragon's breast, and a huge gush of blood showed that he had hit his mark well and truly. The dragon reared and tried to rush on him once again, but the lion was already clinging to his back and biting into the nape of his neck, so that now he had to defend himself against a new attacker. Hans succeeded in thrusting his sword into the monster's chest a second time, and what with the great loss of blood and the lion's deep bite, the dragon's strength began to fail very fast, and it was not long before he was stone dead. Hans cut off the tip of his tongue as a token of victory and put it in his pocket. He told the men who were with him to bring the slaughtered beast to the town, which they were only too glad to do, and then he set off for the town. He saw the coach that was bringing the Princess coming towards him, so he stopped it, jumped on to the box, and drove home. When he reached the outskirts of the town and saw the first townspeople coming to meet him, he threw back the roof of the coach, adorned both coach and horses with flowers, and pressed a wreath of wild flowers on to the Princess' curly hair.

When the people saw their Princess coming safely home, they were wild with joy. A few boys ran on as fast as they could to spread the news.

By the time Hans and the Princess reached the town, a huge crowd had gathered, and all the people rushed joyously towards them and accompanied them to the King's castle, where the King, who had already heard of the dragon's defeat, was waiting for his daughter and her deliverer at the gates. Hans lifted the Princess out of the coach, and the King, overcome with joy, took her in his arms, and led her into the castle, telling Hans to follow.

Hans now had to describe every detail of the fight; and as a proof of the dragon's death, he laid the tip of the tongue before the King. As a reward for his services in rescuing the Princess and saving the whole town, the King promised him the hand of the Princess. Before long, the happy pair were married in great splendour, and they lived happily together for many years.

One day, when they were out riding together, the young couple came upon a valley. Hans asked his wife where it led, but she only answered, "Once in, never out again". To all other questions, she would give no reply. This sounded suspicious to Hans, and he determined to discover what was so mysterious about this valley. One day, when the Princess had no time to come with him, he rode out alone and made his way towards the valley. A snake lay on the path where the valley opened and would not let him pass. He picked up a stone and threw it at the snake, wounding it seriously. Then he rode on, and after some time, he came to a castle. He leapt from his horse and went in. He saw no one, and presently he wandered into a large hall full of stone statues, without meeting a soul. At the other end of the hall was an open fireplace, and as it was cold, he lit a fire and sat down in front of it. The lion, who was always with him, also lay down beside it. Before long, an old woman came hobbling into the hall, carrying a little stick in her hand, and said, "Brr! brr! How cold it is!"

"Come to the hearth and warm yourself," said Hans.

The old woman came near and warmed herself. Then she asked: "May I touch you and the lion once with my little stick?"

"If it would really give you pleasure, then do so!" Hans answered.

The old woman, who was really a wicked witch, did so, and at once all life vanished from Hans and the lion, and they were turned into stone. So now there was one more statue in the hall. And since Hans did not return to his Princess in the castle, she and everyone else believed that some misfortune had befallen him, and they were very sad.

Sepp was the first to come back from his travels. Obedient to his fathers' orders, he went to the lime-tree to see if one of the knives had gone rusty.

Jörg's knife was still untarnished, but Hans' knife was completely eaten away with rust. Then Sepp knew his brother had fallen into danger, and he set out along the road Hans had followed, to go to his aid. When he had travelled some way, he came to the same inn that Hans had visited and, like him, he ordered something to eat and talked to the innkeeper. And when he was ready to go, the innkeeper gave him a tame lion.

Sepp came to the town, and turned in at the inn where Hans had been before him. Since he looked exactly like his brother, the innkeeper took him for Hans, and said:

"Thank goodness you're here again, Hans! Wherever have you been all this time? You might at least have told us where you were going, so that we need not have worried. Make haste to the castle: the Princess will be so pleased that you're back."

Sepp realised immediately that something had happened to his brother in this town, and he tried to discover what he could by asking a few cautious questions. He pretended that he could remember nothing, and in this way he made the innkeeper tell him of Hans' adventures. Then he went on to the King's castle, and even there everyone thought he was Hans, including the Princess herself. She scolded him for going away without telling her, and for staying away so long. But in the end she forgave him, for she was really glad to see her Hans – as she supposed this young man to be.

Meanwhile, Sepp enjoyed himself at her side. One day, they both went for a ride and passed a narrow valley. He asked the Princess where it led; at first she looked at him in amazement, and then she said: "Once in, never out again". To all other questions she would give no answer. Sepp thought this most odd, and made up his mind to find out for himself what was so mysterious about this valley. Soon afterwards, when the Princess had no time to come out, he rode alone to the valley, and there, right in the opening was a snake in the middle of the path, which would not let him pass. Sepp saw it was seriously injured, and he threw a stone at it and wounded it mortally. Then he rode on till he reached the castle. He went in and saw no one. He found his way to the hall where stood many stone statues, one behind the other. But the last one resembled his brother Hans.

Since it was cold in the hall, he lit a fire in the hearth. Soon afterwards a door opened, and in came an old woman, holding a small stick in one hand. "Brr, brr! How cold it is!" she said, and Sepp answered:

"Come here and warm yourself."

"I don't dare," she replied.

"Why not?"

"The lion will bite me."

"He won't do you any harm," said Sepp, "just come here."

So the old woman came nearer and warmed herself. After a time she asked: "May I touch you and your lion with my little stick?"

"No!" said Sepp.

"But I would so love to do it!"

"Oh, then, do so!" he answered.

Hardly had the witch touched Sepp and the lion with the stick when they were both turned to stone. So now Sepp could not return to the town either, and again there was great sorrow everywhere.

Now Jörg came to the lime-tree where the three brothers had buried their knives. First of all, he looked for Sepp's knife, but it was not where he had buried it. Then he looked for Hans' knife; he found that all right, and Sepp's knife near it; both of them were completely rusty. From this he knew that something had happened to his brothers, and that Sepp had already been there, and had gone to Hans' help. He buried the two knives again and set off along Hans' path. Like the others, he came to the house of the innkeeper with the lions, stayed there to eat and talk, and was given a tame lion when he left. When he reached the town, he went to the same inn as the others had visited. The innkeeper, who had in the meantime become a Minister of State, gave him a good talking-to because of his repeated disappearances. Jörg stared at him, stupefied, for he did not know that the innkeeper had mistaken him for Hans, owing to the very close resemblance of the three brothers.

The innkeeper soon realized that Jörg did not understand him. He was sure that the young man before him was really Hans, who had freed the town from the dragon and had married the Princess. He said he might at least explain why he had twice ridden out of the town without taking leave of any one, and come back each time without his horse. Jörg explained that he knew nothing of all this, that his name was not Hans but Jörg, and that he was in the town for the very first time in his life. The innkeeper would not let this pass, and ordered him to accompany him at once to the castle. The Princess, he said, would be pleased to see him again; but now he must not vanish again, but stay in the castle, since the King was already old, and he was to be made King in his place.

Jörg realized that it was no use insisting that he was not Hans, and he went with the innkeeper to the castle. There he was at first scolded; but before long, everyone was rejoicing at his return, including the Princess; and all thought he was Hans.

96

One day, he rode out with the Princess, and when they came near the valley, he too, like his brothers, asked whither it led. The Princess answered as before, "Once in, never out again". But this time she also said, "I've already told you that twice, and from now on I shall never tell you again." Neither of them knew, of course, that both Hans and Sepp were in that valley; and Jörg thought the Princess' answer so very odd that he made up his mind to visit the valley as soon as possible.

Next day, the Princess had no time to go riding, so Jörg set out alone for the valley. He saw a dead snake lying on the path and pushed it aside. When he came to the castle, he got off his horse, went in, and neither met nor saw a single person. At last he came to the hall filled with statues, and saw that of the last two, one resembled Hans and the other Sepp. He realized that a spell had been cast on his brothers, and he determined to lift it, if he could, from them and all the others.

When he grew cold, he lit a fire in the hearth and warmed himself. Soon the same old woman came in and said: "Brr, brr! How cold it is!" Jörg asked her to come and warm herself by the fire; she said she was afraid of the lion, but he calmed her, and she came near the fire. However, when she asked: "May I touch you and the lion with my little stick?" he sprang up and cried:

"No! You are a witch! You have cast a spell on both my brothers and all the others here. If you don't take the spell off them all immediately, I'll let the lion tear you to pieces!"

Since she did not wish to be torn limb from limb, the witch did as she was told. She touched all the statues with her little stick, and they all came back to life again at once. The brothers embraced, while the rest thanked Jörg for saving them.

No one wanted to stay in the castle, so they all set off for the town, taking the witch with them as their prisoner. The three brothers, Hans, Sepp, and Jörg, rode in front, and when they arrived, everyone was astonished to see three young men, so exactly alike. A huge feast was prepared. Jörg was proclaimed the deliverer, and the innkeeper, who had no sons, adopted him as his own. Sepp was given the valley "Once in, never out again", and the castle too; but Hans was made King and ruled wisely and justly together with his wife, who was very glad to have her husband back again, this time for ever.

As for the witch, she was dealt with quickly. She and her little stick were burnt at the stake.

# LUXEMBURG

### MICHEL MICHELKLEINER'S GOOD LUCK

When Michel Michelkleiner was eighteen years old, his father took him aside and said:

"Michel, my son, the time has come for you to try your luck. Be a good boy, pick up this bundle I have made ready for you, and be off."

Michel did as he was told, and with a heavy oak-stick in his hand, he took leave of his father and went down the hillside.

He walked all day without stopping, and so, when evening drew near, his stomach was vexed with hunger, for he had not eaten a mouthful of bread all that time. All the same, he was eager to continue his journey, even when darkness had come. Suddenly, he caught sight of a fire glowing some distance away in the woods.

"Where there is fire," he said to himself, "there are people, Christian people for certain, who are likely to help me."

And he walked briskly in the direction of the fire. When he had come nearer to it, he realized that there was a band of robbers sitting round it, cooking big pieces of meat on the fire. Since he was as hungry as a wolf, his mouth started watering with the delicious smell of grilled meat.

He bade the robbers a hearty good evening before asking for food and drink. But no sooner had they seen him than they pounced upon him, robbed him of his bundle and his clothes down to his underwear, and threw him into a big cask near at hand. This they closed with a heavy cover, and there they left him. After an hour or so, they marched off down the wood, and Michel heard no more noises round his abode.

"Oh, dear," thought the poor boy in despair, "this will be the end of me!" Prayer after prayer arose from his lips. Then all of a sudden he heard a sort of treading-noise, like light steps round the cask. He looked through the bung-hole and saw a dog sniffing again and again at the cask. Michel thrust his hand through the bung-hole and made shift to grasp the dog's tail. He held on tightly, and the terrified dog tried to run away. In doing so, he upset the cask, which rolled a good way down the hillside, and at last broke into a thousand pieces.

So Michel was delivered, and in high spirits he went back up the hill towards the fire. He approached very cautiously, hoping to find some food left over from the robbers' meal. When he had stayed his hunger, he warmed himself by the glowing embers for a while, and after that he felt thoroughly restored and prepared to face any risk.

He walked for many a mile, and presently he saw a light, far off behind the woodside. Soon he came to a hut. He looked inside, and what did he see? Nobody but the gang of robbers who had ill-treated him so badly some hours ago. He saw that they were about to divide their last night's booty among themselves.

"Well, you brethren," he said to himself, "I am going to teach you what it means to bully a poor honest boy like me!"

He climbed up on to the roof, and boldly entered the chimney-pot. But his feet found no firm hold there, and he fell down the chimney on to a heap of logs in the kitchen, roaring and making a noise like a thousand devils bursting out of hell. The robbers in the room were frightened almost to death, for they thought the moment had come when they were to be taken to Hell for their evil deeds. They ran out of the hut as fast as their legs could carry them, never to be seen again.

Meanwhile, Michel recovered a little from his own fright. He opened the door, and was nearly beside himself with pleasure when he saw how many heaps of gold and silver the robbers had left on the table when they ran off, mad with terror. He looked around him and saw a bag in a corner. In it were his clothes, which he put on again, and then, filling his pockets with the money, he took to his heels through thickets and open fields, and arrived home at the end of the second day.

The good people in his neighbourhood wondered how a simple village boy could have earned so much money in so short a time.


## MASTER SLY

A long time ago, seven wealthy farmers and one very poor man lived in a village. The seven farmers were stupid, whereas the poor man was clever, and for this reason he was called Master Sly. The rich villagers hated their poor neighbour so much that, to make an end of him, they plotted together to make life impossible for him. They made up their minds to kill his good old mother, who cooked his meals, baked bread, and did the washing for him. No sooner decided upon than done: one day, when Master Sly returned home, he found his beloved mother dead on the floor.

9·

After some thought, he tied her corpse on his donkey's back and started off towards the town. On the way he saw from afar a heavy cart loaded with all kinds of goods coming towards him. He left the road and hid behind the hedge, leaving the donkey to keep the track as well as it could. However, the donkey was too silly to avoid the cart, and the carter, thinking the old woman on its back was asleep, shouted to her as loud as he could:

"Get out of my way, you beggar of an old witch, or I'll make you learn better!"

Yet she did not even move. Wild with anger, the carter called out to her: "I'll teach you how to behave to decent folk on the road!" and he hit her so hard with his whip that she fell from the donkey's back to the ground, and lay there motionless.

Suddenly, Master Sly leapt out from his hiding-place, crying and lamenting aloud:

"Now you've done it! You've killed my mother who kept my house, carefully and honestly. O, what will come from this evil deed?"

"Good heavens!" cried the carter, quite horrified. "We must both keep silent about these ill-doings. I shall be hanged if people get to know about this. If you will consent to hold your tongue, I will let you have this cart, with the load on it, and the four horses as well."

"If you do that," answered Master Sly, "I swear to you that nothing will be known of this mischief. Go on your way, and mind what you say."

So they separated on good terms.

Master Sly returned to the village in glory, with his cart and four horses. When he was asked about his good fortune, he answered coolly:

"Didn't I sell my dead mother to townspeople, and didn't they give me so much money for her that I could afford to buy this cart and its load and the four horses with the money?"

Now the blockheads who heard him took counsel together, and they ran home to kill their aged womenfolk, all of them, mother and grandmother as well, and carried them to town. But imagine their surprise when they were sent to prison for murder!

After some years, they were released from prison and returned home. They found Master Sly still clever and well at ease, yet as poor as he had been before, in spite of his cart and his horses, and the money he had owned when they saw him last.

Mad for revenge, they decided to demolish his baking-oven, hoping that he would not be able to live without bread. When they had done

100

so, they left the broken bricks lying on the ground. Master Sly filled a sack with the rubble and took it to the town, where he spent the night at an inn. Before he went to bed, he impressed on the landlady that she must take good care of the sack, as there were valuables in it about which it was not wise to let people know.

During the night, the landlady opened the sack, and thought she saw a great many lumps of gold. She asked her husband to lend her a hand in taking the gold out of the sack and filling it with bars of silver instead.

Early next morning, Sly went home again, and showed his silver to all and everybody. When the villagers enquired how he had managed to get so much silver in the space of a night, he replied:

"Well, then, didn't I sell the smashed bricks to townspeople?"

Once again the foolish people ran home and demolished their baking-ovens, and next morning they offered the rubble to the townspeople. But the townsmen only laughed at them.

After that, they decided to get rid of Master Sly by drowning him in the village pond. They tied him up in a bed-cloth and took him down to the pond. Sly begged them to allow him enough time to make his peace with God, so they went about their usual business for about an hour.

In the meantime, Master Sly had started shouting like a madman:

"No, I don't want her! No, I don't want her! No, I never!"

A man came by on horseback, and hearing Sly's shouts, he asked whom he did not want.

"Well," said Master Sly, "I am being urged into marrying the King's daughter, which I don't want to do."

"Listen to me, good man," said the horseman, eagerly, "you mount my horse, and let me take your place in the bed-cloth, well tied up."

Sly did as he was asked, and went off to hide in a wood close by. After a while, the villagers came back for him, and the man in the bed-cloth kept crying out:

"Yes, I want her! I do want her!"

"You'll get her very soon," answered the villagers, laughingly, and they took the cloth with the horseman in it and threw him into the pond.

They could hardly believe their eyes when, turning back homewards, they saw their hated neighbour riding up to them on a white horse, as proudly as a squire.

"Are there any more horses of that kind in the pond?" they asked him.

"I am sure there are," he replied. "Look here and see!" And going near the pond, he showed them the reflection of his horse on the smooth surface of the water. After that, each one of them tried to outdo his rivals in catching hold of the mock-horse in the pond, and so all the seven jumped into the water and were drowned.

As for Master Sly, he rode home to his village and lived there peacefully and undisturbed for the rest of his life, up to his blessed end.

# HOLLAND

## "WITHOUT WORRY"

One day a King was out riding, a habit which Kings usually have. He came to a farmhouse, and on the gate-post were the words: "Without Worry".

"That's strange," thought the King. "I am the head of the country and I have plenty of worries. Is it possible that there is someone living without worries?"

He went to the farmer's wife and said:

"My good woman, how are you?"

"I am fine, sir," she answered, "and how are you?"

"I am fine too," said the King, "and do you like living here?"

"Yes, it's not so bad," said the woman.

"And have you any worries?" asked the King.

"You may not think so, sir," she said, "but I have a lot of boys who have to be fed, clothed, and looked after, and that is a big problem."

"How it is possible then," said the King, "that you have written on your gate, 'Without Worry'?"

"Oh, that wasn't my idea," said the farmer's wife. "Our master had that put there."

"Who is your master?" asked the King.

"Mr. So-and-So," she said, naming one of the King's bodyguards.

"Will you say that again?" he said.

She repeated the name, and now the King was sure who was the owner of the farmhouse.

The next day he ordered the man to come to him.

"Are you getting on all right?" he asked him.

"Fairly well, sir," said the man.

"Is that your farmhouse?" went on the King.

"Yes, sir," answered the man.

"Haven't you any worries?"

"No, sir. I can't complain. I get a good weekly wage from you. I have some money of my own, so what more do I want?"

"Then I will tell you something," said the King. "I have plenty of

103

worries, and I can't have anybody working for me who has none. You must leave my service at once, without notice."

That was a shock for the man, and he begged the King to reconsider his decision. After a while, the King consented to do so, but only if the man could answer the following questions within three days:

"How many shovels would you need to empty the sea?"

"How many days would it take to ride round the Earth?"

"Can you read my thoughts?"

How cheerful that man used to be, how unhappy he was now! With drooping shoulders he came face to face with one of his mates, who happened to look rather like him.

"What's the matter?" asked his friend. "You look as though you had killed someone."

The man told him what had happened.

"Wouldn't you be upset?" he asked.

"Well, no," said his mate. "We'll change clothes, and I'll fix everything up for you."

They changed clothes, and on the third day the friend went to the King.

"Have you the answers?" asked the King. "How many shovels would you need to empty the sea?"

"One shovel," said the man, "if it is a big one."

"That's clever," said the King. "How many days would it take you to ride round the world?"

"Twenty-four hours," said the man, "if you sat on the sun."

"That's very clever too," said the King, "and can you read my thoughts?"

"You think I am So-and-So," answered the man, "but I am his mate."

Then the King had to laugh, for he saw he had been outwitted, and he consented to allow So-and-So to stay on in his service.


## THE THREE PEDLARS

Once upon a time there were three pedlars. They trudged behind each other, along the sandy road of the Hessenweg, which leads to Doesburg, with their pedlar's boxes on their back, and an oak stick in their hands. It was in the middle of May, and it was terribly hot between the fir-trees and the high coppice, and the sweat was pouring down from under their caps, falling in streaks on to their blue hessen blouses.

"Good heavens, what heat!" said the man in front, and he threw his pedlar's box on the ground.

"Let us go to sleep for a while," said the second.

"Shame on you!" said the third; and they all fell down in the heather with their heads on their boxes.

"The first inn we come to, I'm taking a quick one," said the first.

"Me, too, I'm all for it."

"You two can squander your money, you have three pennies each, and I have only one."

"What an ass you are!" said the first.

"Yes, a fool, that's what you are," said the second.

"What's all this about?" said the third. "Are you two at it again? If I were you, I would shut my mouth. I won't take what is not due to me. Now you know it."

"You are a stupid fool. You have to use your brains. I'm telling you, it's everyone for himself."

"Sure, I agree, everyone thinks about himself, and charity begins at home."

"Well, you two can say what you like, I don't care; but I'll get more from my honest penny than you two will with your three dishonest pennies."

"All right, have it your own way."

"Well, I bet my pedlar's box that I'll go further with my one honest penny than you two ruffians with three."

They agreed to the bet, and to seal it, they hit each other on the hands which were pouring with sweat. They stood up and went on their way, and they came to an inn. They went inside, ordered a drink, finished it in one gulp, and paid one penny. When they came out again, the first one said:

"Now tell me, how far have you got with your one honest penny! I knew beforehand that we should win with our three pennies. You are already broke. Give us your box."

They divided the socks and stockings, and threw the box in the ditch.

"Now you can sing for your supper!" They jeered and mocked him, and made fun of him.

"Now you don't need to worry about carrying that heavy load any more, ha! ha! ha!"

"I dare to bet my two eyes."

"All right, we agree to that." And again they hit each others' hands.

"All right then, on we go."

Their heavy spiked boots pierced the dry dusty road, their sticks marking time as they trudged along with their loads on their backs. The road ran through a dark birch and pine forest.

"Look! What do I see! A new straw roof there, behind those three lime-trees and the horse-trough."

"I smell gin."

"I believe you're right. Shall we step in?"

"Well, yes, don't let it get stale. I'm dying of thirst."

They threw down their boxes, lifted the latch, jumped on two stools by the counter, and ordered two drinks from the barman. The honest one walked on as though he had heard nothing. His strength left him, and he mumbled to himself:

"God in heaven! Could these two drunkards be right?"

Just then the two came jogging along with red faces and gleaming eyes, as though the Devil was in them.

"There you are, you thought you could run away, since you have lost your bet again. Don't pretend to yourself, we'll deal with you."

One plunged his hand in his trouser-pocket and took out a pointed knife, the other caught him by the throat, and they picked out both his eyes.

Along the side of the road was a row of beautiful fir-trees, and under one of these trees was a gallows. They dragged him there and threw him down, so that he fell full length on the ground.

"There, you old rascal, you have got what was coming to you, and see how far your honest penny brought you!"

"We've settled that all right," said one of the rogues when they were on their road again. "Nobody will know anything about it, and we have his socks and stockings."

The sun was setting, leaving a beautiful red glow in the sky, but for the honest one, everything was dark in the woods. He was shivering, and he crept close to the gallows, as though he was afraid they would see him and return to hurt him still more.

Clap, clap, clap! A huge crow flew down and settled on the top of the old oak-tree above the gallows.

Clap, clap, clap again.

"So, sisters, are you there?"

"Yes, we have been waiting for you. What is the matter?"

"All those who are blind will be able to see, because a magic dew will fall tonight. The King's daughter is ill, but she will get better if she cooks and uses the herbs that are growing behind the King's garden. Whoever can cure her can marry her."

"Good night, sisters." Clap, clap, clap.

"Good night, sisters." Clap, clap, clap.

The honest pedlar was very puzzled when he heard this, and a few minutes later he was creeping around, striking his hand on the bushes, and then drawing it across his forehead. Three times he did this, and then he opened his eyes and saw the stars between the tops of the trees. He stood up, shook the pine needles from his trousers, and walked through the woods to reach the main road. But he had lost his way; and suddenly he came to a beautiful lane, long and broad, and then, when the sun began to shine, he found himself all at once standing beside a huge gate. It had golden railings, padlock and handle, and a man was standing there, with beautiful gold buttons on his coat and a long weapon in his hand. And there, far behind the guard, was a great and beautiful castle.

The honest man could hardly believe his eyes, he was so amazed, and he stood there with his mouth open, as though at any minute he would swallow the guard. When he pulled himself together again, he cried: "Well, I never!" He gazed at the magnificent sight, and then he walked to the gate.

"Hello, there!" he said; and when the guard looked his way, he asked him if the King was out of bed.

"What do you want?" asked the guard.

"Nothing, I just want to know if the King is up yet or still lying in bed."

"What do you want from the King?"

"His daughter is ill, and I want to cure her."

The guard thought, "That's strange, How does this man know?" He turned the lock three times, and the honest man entered.

"Don't worry," he said, "I won't make a noise. Show me where the King's garden is, and bring me a tin or a pot that I can cook in."

Quickly he cooked the herbs for the King's daughter. She drank the brew, and immediately she was better again.

Three days later they were married, and they ate their meal from golden plates, and drank wine from golden tumblers, and all the high court people bowed to him. The honest man had everything he could wish for, a good-looking wife (although she was small), money, and grandeur in everything from new trousers to boots. Inwardly he was in his glory, although, to suit his position, he always had to look a little sour.

One Tuesday morning, he got up early to go hunting. When he got to the gate, two men were standing there, looking very scruffy. Just as he was about to say good morning, he had a shock, for he recognized the two men as those who had so ill-treated him. But he never thought of paying them back for their cruelty. He only felt sorry for them. He took them into the kitchen and let them eat as much meat and bacon as they could, and related to them his story in all its details. They both listened with big ears, and when they left, they went to the gallows in the woods to eavesdrop on the crows' conversation.

Clap, clap, clap, came the first crow. Clap, clap, clap.

"Hello, sister, I believe someone is listening to us. I smell danger!"

Three days later, they found two dead men on the hill. It was a terrible sight, bones and flesh were lying around, and they had no eyes.

They didn't get very far with their dishonest pennies. Just about ten steps from the gallows.


## THE WONDER CHILD

There was once a Queen who greatly longed to have a baby. Every morning she went to a quiet place in the garden and prayed to God to send her a child, but her prayers were not answered. Then one morning, when she was praying in the garden, an angel suddenly appeared before her, and said:

"Don't be afraid. Your prayers have been heard, and when nine new moons have passed, you will bear a child, and he will be a Wonder Child. Whatever he wishes for will be granted to him."

The Queen was overjoyed by this news, and she ran to tell the King; and, as you can imagine, he too was as happy as though he had found a piece of gold.

When nine new moons had passed, the Queen had her baby, the most beautiful baby-boy in the world. Every morning she took him walking in the garden. He grew like a cabbage, and his skin was the colour of peaches and cream. The people of the court loved him so much that they could have eaten him – so beautiful a baby he was.

Now, the Queen's cook was a man of very bad character, and he often said to himself, when he looked at the baby, "If I had that boy, I could take advantage of his miraculous powers."

One day, when it was very hot, the Queen fell asleep on the garden seat, and the cook quietly stole the baby away, and spread blood on her skirt. He took the child to a hut in the woods where he could be looked

108

after safely. Then he went back to the King, and told him that a wild animal had eaten the boy, because the Queen had not watched over him properly. The King was terribly angry, and he gave orders that the Queen was to be imprisoned in a dark cellar and left there to starve to death.

But our heavenly Lord knew she was not guilty, and every day he sent two angels in the form of white doves, who came down from Heaven and brought her food and drink.

Seven years passed. The cook thought that the time had now come when he could use the Wonder Child, so he gave the King notice and went away to the hut where the boy was hidden. He said to him:

"Little one, wish now for a big beautiful palace, with a beautiful garden full of flowers, an orchard and a lake and a summer-house, and everything."

The boy did so, and his wish was fulfilled.

Time went on, and then the cook said to the boy:

"Wish now for a playmate, the most beautiful girl you can imagine."

The boy did so, as before. Hardly were the words of his wish spoken when there stood before them a girl so beautiful that no painter could have thought of any one lovelier.

The two children played together every day, and grew very fond of each other. The cook lived in the palace like a lord, drinking in the morning, hunting in the afternoon, and drinking again in the evening. But all the same, he was not easy in his mind. He was afraid in his heart that the boy, who was growing more sensible and thoughtful every day, would begin to long for his father and mother, and if he did, it would be fatal for the cook.

So one day he said to the boy's playmate:

"When the Prince goes to sleep, go in quietly and stab him through the heart. If you don't do this, you won't have long to live, for you will die instead of him. When you have killed him, you must bring me his heart and his tongue, to prove that you have done it."

The girl could not bring herself to do this, for the two children loved each other very much. She made up her mind to disobey the order. There was a young goat in the stall that had not long been born, and this she had slaughtered. Then she told the Prince to hide himself, and she took the goat's heart and tongue to the cook.

The cook did not trust her, and he went to look for the Prince who was hidden in bed under the blankets. The boy jumped up immediately and said:

"I wish you to be changed into a black poodle, and to be unable to eat anything but burning charcoals, so that the flames will burn your mouth. You must wear a gold chain round your neck, that I may always recognize you."

No sooner had he uttered these words than the cook was changed into a black dog. The girl told the servant to set burning charcoals before him, and the flames burnt up all round his mouth.

The young Prince began to long for his mother. He could not overcome this longing, so one day he said to his playmate:

"I am going back to my home, and if you like, you can come with me."

The girl didn't like the thought of the long journey, and she asked the Prince to change her into a flower, which he did. He put the flower in his buttonhole, took his walking-stick, and started on his journey home, with his black poodle following behind him.

After a long journey and many adventures, they came to the locked cellar where his mother was. Through the small window, he called:

"Darling mother, respected Queen, are you still alive?"

The Queen thought one of the two doves who brought her daily food was speaking, and she answered: "I have eaten enough, dear angel!"

"I am not talking about that," said the Prince. "I am your son who was supposed to have been eaten by a wild animal. But that was a lie; I am still alive, and here beside you."

Then the Prince went to the King and asked him if he needed a hunter.

"Yes," said the King, "but there are so few wild animals in my woods."

"That doesn't matter," replied the Prince. "I can still catch them."

"Well," said the King, "I should like to see that," and he called his men together and they all went off to hunt.

When they reached the woods, the Prince wished for wild animals to come from all corners – hares, rabbits, deer, and wild pigs. Within half an hour the cart was filled with wild animals. The King immediately organized a great feast. His larders hadn't been so full for years, and the new hunter was given the right-hand place of honour beside the King.

After they had all had a good meal, the Prince wished that one of the Court Marshalls should mention his mother. Hardly had he done so when one of the Marshalls stood up and said:

"Your Majesty, we have everything to our liking here, but how is the poor Queen faring? Is she still living or has she starved to death?"

The King became very angry and said:

110

"Don't speak about the Queen; she was the cause of my little boy being eaten by a wild animal."

Then the new hunter stood up and said:

"I am your son, and my mother is still alive. The wild animals didn't eat me; but the cook, that old scoundrel, kidnapped me and spread blood on my mother's skirt."

He pulled the poodle in front of the King, and ordered a pot of burning charcoals to be brought to the dog, who ate them, and the flames smothered his mouth.

The King asked his son to change the dog back to his former shape, and at once the cook was standing there in his white apron, his white cap on his head, and a big knife in his hand. The King ordered his arrest, and he was thrown into prison.

Then the Prince said:

"Father, would you like to see the girl who has looked after me since I was kidnapped, and who saved my life when the cook ordered her to kill me?"

The King said "Yes", and the Prince took the flower from his button-hole and showed it to his father, who said he had never seen such a beautiful flower. Then the Prince changed it into a young and lovely girl.

The King sent his Marshalls to fetch the Queen from the cellar and bring her back to the castle. But she did not want to join the feast, nor did she want anything to eat or drink.

"Our dear Lord in Heaven," she said, "didn't forget me when I was imprisoned in the cellar, and now He is coming to fetch me."

And so it happened. Three days afterwards, the Queen died. When she was taken to the cemetery, two white doves flew above the coffin. They were the angels who had brought food to her when she was in prison.

The King ordered the cook to be cut to pieces; and soon afterwards he too died, of a broken heart, and he too was taken to the cemetery.

The Prince became King. He married his sweetheart who became Queen, and they ruled their land for many, many years; and if they are not dead, then they will be living there still, having a long and happy life.

## CHRIST AND PETER

It happened long ago, when Our Lord was walking with Peter. It was getting dark, and they wanted to stay overnight at a farmhouse. They saw a shepherd lying against a tree with his sheep, and Peter asked him which was the shortest way to the farmhouse where they wanted to stay. Shepherds have the name of being lazy, and this one was too lazy even to stand up and point the way. He just lay on the ground without moving, and said: "Go that way and along there."

"We still don't know which way to go," said Our Lord. They went on a little farther, and presently they saw a house. A girl was standing by the wall.

"Shall I ask her?" said Our Lord, and he said to the girl: "Which is the shortest way to the farmhouse?"

She sprang up at once and ran backwards and forwards, waving her arms while she pointed the way.

"You go here, and along there," she said.

"Well, well," said Peter. "What a difference between her and the last person we asked!"

"Those two should get married," remarked Our Lord. "What the one is short of, the other makes up for!"

They walked on and arrived at the farmhouse. They asked for a bed, and were told they could have one if they would get up at three o'clock in the morning and help with the threshing.

When it was time to get up in the morning, they were so tired that they stayed in bed. The farmer saw them there and determined to make them get up.

"Stay in bed," whispered Our Lord to Peter.

The farmer was so angry that he took a stick and started beating Peter on the back.

"We will still stay in bed," whispered Our Lord to Peter again, "but we will change places, and I will lie in front."

"All right," said Peter.

The farmer came back a second time, and again he took the stick in his hand. He muttered to himself:

"The first time I hit the one in the front of the bed; now I will hit the back one."

So Peter was beaten again. Then Our Lord decided that they would get up and help with the threshing, and they took a lantern and went to the shed.

112

"Give me that candle and put out the lantern," said Our Lord.

He took the candle and put it beside the bunch of straw, and the grain started running out of the straw. The farmer and his men looked on amazed, for this was a wonder.

"Is it good?" he asked.

Yes, it was good.

Then they got on with the threshing. Presently Our Lord said to Peter:

"Look, they are going to try it too. These people are so stupid, you will soon see the flames shooting over the shed."

And it was so. Before long the shed was on fire.

"They have their deserts," said Our Lord. "They have given us a beating, and this is their reward."

# ENGLAND

## THE SMALL-TOOTH DOG

Once upon a time there was a merchant who travelled about the world a great deal. On one of his journeys, thieves attacked him, and they would have taken both his life and his money if a large dog had not come to his rescue and driven the thieves away.

When the dog had driven the thieves off, he took the merchant to his house, which was a very handsome one, and he dressed his wounds and nursed him till he was well.

As soon as he was able to travel, the merchant began his journey home, but before starting he told the dog how grateful he was for his kindness, and asked him what reward he could offer in return, and he said he would not refuse to give him the most precious thing that he had.

And so the merchant said to the dog, "Will you accept a fish that I have that can speak twelve languages?"

"No," said the dog, "I will not."

"Or a goose that lays golden eggs?"

"No," said the dog, "I will not."

"Or a mirror in which you can see what anybody is thinking?"

"No," said the dog, "I will not."

"Then what will you have?" said the merchant.

"I will have none of such presents," said the dog, "but let me fetch your daughter and take her to my house."

When the merchant heard this he was grieved, but what he had promised had to be done, so he said to the dog, "You can come and fetch my daughter after I have been home for a week."

So at the end of the week, the dog came to the merchant's house to fetch his daughter, but when he got there, he stayed outside the house and would not come in. But the merchant's daughter did as her father told her, and came out of the house dressed for a journey and ready to go with the dog.

When the dog saw her, he looked pleased and said, "Jump on my back," and away they went at a great pace until they reached the dog's house which was many miles off.

114

But after she had been a month at the dog's house she began to mope and cry.

"What are you crying for?" said the dog.

"Because I want to go back to my father," she said.

The dog said, "If you promise me that you will not stay at home more than three days, I will take you there. But first of all," he said, "tell me what you call me."

"Oh," she said, "your name is Sweet-as-a-honeycomb."

So he trotted away with her on his back for forty miles, when they came to a stile.

"And what do you call me?" said he, before they got over the stile. And thinking she was safe on her way, the girl said, "A great, foul, small-tooth dog."

But when she said this, he did not jump over the stile, but turned right round about at once, and galloped back to his own house with the girl on his back.

Another week went by, and again the girl wept so bitterly that the dog promised her again to take her to her father's house. So she got on his back again, and they reached the first stile as before, and then the dog stopped and said, "And what do you call me?"

"Sweet-as-a-honeycomb," she replied. Then the dog leapt over the stile, and they went on for twenty miles until they came to another stile.

"And what do you call me?" said the dog, with a wag of his tail. She was thinking more of her father and her own home than of the dog, so she answered, "A great, foul, small-tooth dog."

Then the dog was in a great rage, and he turned right round about and galloped back to his own house as before. After that she cried for another week, and the dog promised again to take her back to her father's house. So she mounted upon his back once more, and when they got to the first stile, the dog asked, "And what do you call me?"

"Sweet-as-a-honeycomb," she said.

So he jumped over the stile, and away they went – for now the girl had made up her mind to say the most loving things she could think of – until they reached her father's house. When they got to the door of the merchant's house, the dog said, "And what do you call me?"

Just at that moment, the girl forgot the loving things she meant to say and began, "A great ..." but the dog began to turn, and she got fast hold of the door latch, and was going to say "Foul", when she saw how grieved the dog looked, and remembered how good and patient he had been with her, so she said, "Sweet-as-a-honeycomb."

10·

When she said this, she thought the dog would be content and gallop away, but instead of that he suddenly stood up on his hind legs, and with his fore-legs he pushed off his dog's head and threw it high in the air. His hairy coat dropped off, and there stood the handsomest young man in the world, with the finest and smallest teeth you ever saw.

Of course they were married, and lived together happily.

## KING ARTHUR AND THE DRAGON

Once, long ago, when the high tide used to come right over Carr Marshes to the foot of Dunster Castle, a great serpent lived in the wet marshes, and came out to kill men and cattle all over the countryside. At length the people sent to King Arthur in Camelot and asked him to rid the country of it. He came himself, and rode down to Carhampton and the marshes, but the creature hid itself away, and search as the King might, he could not find any trace of it. As he was riding along by Carhampton (or some say, Cleeve), he saw a strange table-like thing of coloured marble floating in the water. He drew it to land and found engraved upon it the words "The Altar of St. Carantacus". He remembered then how the story went that St. Carantacus had flung his massy altar into the River Severn, and meant to build a church where it came to land. So King Arthur covered it carefully and rode on.

After a while he met a stranger, who asked him if he had seen the altar of Carantacus.

"Who are you?" asked the King, for he did not wish the holy altar to fall into the hands of some sorcerer.

"I am Carantacus," replied the stranger.

Arthur still mistrusted him, and said: "If you are indeed the saint, call up the Dragon I am hunting from his hiding-place, and I will show you the altar."

The stranger turned to the marsh and said a secret word, and at once the whole bog heaved, and a wave of mud came up with a great stench at their feet. Out of it came the Dragon. It crawled up to the saint, who tied his stole round its neck. Then King Arthur led the way to the altar. St. Carantacus followed, with the Dragon crawling meekly behind. Where the altar lay the King gave twelve portions of land for a church, but the altar itself he took back to Camelot, and made into his Round Table. But what came to the Dragon is more than any one now remembers.

116

## KING ARTHUR AND THE WHITE HORSE

There was once a farmer who lived at Mobberley. He had a white horse
that he wished to sell, and he decided to take it to Macclesfield on next
market day. So off he went, leading the horse, down the road and over
the sharp rise of Alderley Edge on his way to the market town. But he
had not got very far along the Edge before he saw an old man with a
long white beard coming towards him.

"Where are you going?" said the old man, and the farmer replied: "To
Macclesfield, to sell my horse."

"I will buy it," said the stranger. But the farmer, seeing he looked poor
and unlikely to be able to afford a good price, refused to sell it to him.

"You are making a mistake," said the old man. "You will not sell it
at Macclesfield today."

But the farmer would not listen, and off he went with his horse. When
he got to the market, he found the stranger's words were true, for no
one bought his horse, and back again he had to go in the evening, still
leading the horse and without any money in his pocket. Half-way over
the Edge, he saw the old man again.

"Will you sell me your horse now?" he asked, and this time the farmer
was only too glad to agree.

"Follow me, then," said the old man, and away he went, with the
farmer following, past Seven Firs and Stormy Point and Saddle Boll,
till they came to a great rock in the hillside. The stranger touched it
with his staff, and immediately iron gates appeared in it, opening into
a cavern. The farmer was frightened, but the old man strode on ahead,
and he was ashamed not to follow. Through many caverns they went
until at last they came to one far larger than the rest. There in a great
circle were many warriors asleep, and with them one taller, handsomer,
and more noble-looking than his fellows. Behind each warrior stood a
white horse, the finest animals imaginable, but one warrior had no horse.
The old man took the farmer's horse, saying it was to fill this place that
it was wanted. But now the farmer was really afraid.

"Who are they?" he whispered, hardly daring to speak lest these
terrible men should wake.

"They are King Arthur and his men," said the old man, "and they
sleep here until the day of need. They will wake when George, son of
George, is King, and then they will ride out to save their country."

When the man heard these words, he was overcome with terror, and
without waiting to hear any more, he fled from the cave, leaving his

horse behind. He was only too glad to get into the clear light of evening, and see the familiar world he knew again, though now he had neither horse nor money. And as he fled out upon the Edge, he heard the iron gates clang to behind him, but he did not stop to look back. Away he went as fast as he could, and never stopped running till he came to his home in Mobberley.

Since that day, no one has ever seen the iron gates again, or the old man either. And since King Arthur has not yet ridden out, it must be supposed that he and his men and his horses, with the farmer's horse among them, are still asleep in Alderley Edge, waiting for the appointed day of waking.

## THE TIDDY MUN

In the old days, before the dykes were made, the Cars were full of boggarts and Will-o'-the-Wisps, and such-like, voices of dead folks and hands without arms, and todlowries and witches, and the folk shook with ague, and dared not venture over the bogs on dark nights; but there was one thing among all the awesome, uncanny ones that made up for all, and that was the Tiddy Mun. He dwelt deep down in the green water-holes and came out at evening when the mists rose. Then he came creeping out in the darkling, limpelty, lopelty, like a dearie wee old granfer, with long white hair and a long white beard, all matted and tangled, and a long grey gown, so that they could hardly see him in the dusk, but they could hear him, whistling like the wind and laughing like a peeweet. He was not wicked like the others, but he was eerie enough, though the times were when he helped them. For in wet seasons, when the water rose to their doorsteps, the whole family would go out together, and shivering in the darkness, they would call:

> Tiddy Mun wi'out a name,
> Thy watters thruff.

They would call it till they heard a cry like a peeweet across the marsh, and then they would go home. Next morning the waters would be down. So when the Dutchmen came to drain the marshes, with great promises of all the good that would come of it, the fen-men would not listen to them, for they knew their Tiddy Mun could never live on a dried marsh. But for all they could do, the Dutchmen worked on, though one after another would vanish away, fetched by the Tiddy Mun. Still more came, and the ditches were dry, and the Cars grew drier and drier, and at last the Tiddy Mun was angry with the Car-men as well as the Dutchies, and the cattle began to die, and the milk curdled, and the children pined and died in their mothers' arms.

At first the Car-men thought the evil was from bogles or witches, but at last it came to them that it was the Tiddy Mun himself. They got together, with their wives and little, pining children, and everyone carried a stoup of water in his hand. They came together to the dyke-edge, and poured the water out, and cried all together:

> Tiddy Mun wi'out a name,
> Here's watter for thee,
> Tak thy spell undone.

It was dead still at first as they listened, and then a great wailing and whimpering broke out all around them, and the mothers cried out that it was the babies they had lost, begging the Tiddy Mun to lift the spell. They said that little hands touched them, and cold lips kissed them, and soft wings fluttered round them in the dark. Then it was silent, and then the peeweet's cry came over the water, and they knew the Tiddy Mun was lifting the spell. They turned back, laughing and crying with joy, and the men ran home like bairns out of school. Only the mothers followed, crying for the wee babies they had lost.

From that day the spell lifted from the Cars and all began to prosper. Only, every Full Moon, men, women and children went out, emptied their stoups of water, and said their rhyme. Those who did not go, but stayed at home, sickened and pined away. But the Cars are dry now, and maybe the Tiddy Mun is frightened away. For no one goes out at the Full Moon now.

# WALES

## THE GWRAIG AND THE THREE BLOWS

There was once a young farmer who lived with his widowed mother near the Black Mountains, and used to graze his cattle near the Lake of Fan Fach. One day, while he was eating his dinner by the lakeside, he saw a most beautiful lady sitting on the surface of the water, combing her long golden hair. He walked down to the lake-edge, as if drawn by a spell, and held out his bread and cheese to her. She looked at him, smiling, and said, "Your bread is too hard, you are not for me." And as she spoke she vanished under the water.

He searched and called, but could hear and see no more of her. He went home and told his tale to his mother, who said the lady was a Gwraig, a Lake-Maiden. She told him to take unbaked dough next day, and see if she liked that better. He did so, and after a long wait, he saw her again, and offered her the dough and cheese, with his heart's love. She said, "Your bread's too soft, you are not for me", but she gave him so sweet a glance before she vanished that he was left not quite without hope.

Next day, on his mother's advice, he took some lightly-baked bread to the lake. He waited until evening before the Gwraig appeared and then she took his bread, ate it, and said, "Your bread is good, you are the man for me." Immediately afterwards, she darted away into the water, and the young man was just about to plunge in after her, when a stately and noble old man rose from the lake and walked towards him, leading a lovely girl in each hand.

"My daughter tells me," he said, "that you wish to marry her. You shall do so if you can tell her from her sister."

The young man looked at the two girls, who where so exactly alike that no one could tell one from the other. But the one on the left moved her foot slightly forward, and then he saw that her sandals were differently laced from those of her sister. He had seen that lacing on that very day, and so he knew she was the maiden of his choice.

"This is my love," he said.

"You have chosen rightly," said the father. "She is yours so long as you treat her well; but if you give her three causeless blows, however light, you will never see her again."

Then he told her to count her dowry, and she counted five and five and five, as long as one breath lasted, and as quick as she counted, sheep appeared. She did the same for cattle and horses, so that the farmer went home with great riches as well as a bride. They were very happy together and had three fine sons. The husband and wife loved each other dearly; but she had strange, unhuman ways, that were a great vexation to him. Once they went together to a christening, and all through it, while the company were making merry, the Gwraig sighed and dabbed her eyes. At last, the farmer tapped her on the shoulder and said: "What are you doing? Can't you make merry like the rest?"

"Why should I rejoice," she said, "when the poor child is born into a world of grief and sorrow? And you have struck me the first blow."

A few months later the baby died, and they went to its funeral. The Gwraig laughed and sang until her scandalized husband tapped her sharply on the shoulder and said: "Be quiet. This is a house of grief."

"How can I grieve," said she, "when the baby has gone out of this world of sorrow to be happy for ever? And that's the second blow."

After that her husband was very careful never to strike her, however gently. They went on happily for years, until he had almost forgotten the need for caution. Then one day they went to a wedding between a young girl and an old miser. In the middle of the festivities, the Gwraig burst into tears and wrung her hands, crying, "Oh, how can you all rejoice when youth and beauty are wedded to old age, not for love but for gold?" All the guests were horrified, and her husband pushed her and said sharply, "Be quiet."

She looked at him very sadly and said: "That's the third blow. Goodbye." No sooner had she said it than she darted from the room, and as she went she called to the cattle, three miles away. They all heard her and followed. Even the slaughtered calf came down from the meathook, and the two oxen who were ploughing came too, dragging the plough behind them. They all went with her to the lake and plunged in headlong after her, leaving a deep furrow behind them on the ground which is shown to this day, though it is eight centuries old.

The farmer never saw his loved wife again; but she came back sometimes in secret to visit her sons. She showed them the use of herbs and taught them deep mysteries of medicine, which were afterwards handed down from father to son in the family, and made the Physicians of Myddvai famous for seven centuries.

# SCOTLAND

## THE KING OF THE BLACK ART

Once upon a time there was an old fisherman, and his old wife, and they had a little house at the side of the mouth of a big river, where he used to go out fishing with his nets every day for his living. So one day he went down to the water-side, and he saw a thing like a box floating on the tide; and he put out a big long stick and carefully pulled it in. And this was a box, sealed up so that no water could get into it, and there was a small child in it – a boy child.

So the man looked at this box in surprise, he didn't know where it had come from, because years ago there weren't as many houses and inhabited places as there are now – and the place where the fisherman was living was a kind of wilderness. And sections of the country were owned by kings, and one thing and another, like that.

But his wife had never had any family, and he lifted this little child out – there was a shawl or an old blanket round it, you see, to keep it warm. And he carried it up to the little house where his wife was, and he went in, and he said: "Look what I've got you!"

She says, "What is it?" And she says, "What are you wanting now? Are you not down doing your work," she says, "and getting something to eat, without coming in tormenting me at this time of the morning! I thought you'd be away out in your boat fishing at this time."

He says, "Look what I got you," he says.

And she turned round, and she nearly fell on the floor when she saw the young infant in her husband's arms. So she takes the child, and she unwinds the shawl, and goes and gets milk for it, and heats milk, and feeds it, one way and another.

So time rolls by, and the child grows to a good size. She rears it as if it were her own, and the old man, he's going on with his fishing, day in and day out. And the boy grew to a good size, and he used to help the father to mend his nets, and scraped the boat when it was needing a cleaning, and one thing and another, like that, till the boy reached the age of maybe about thirteen or fourteen.

But one day, he and the old man are down at the boat, and they see a ship coming in. And on the bridge of this ship there was a man standing, and he was flinging three poison balls with spikes on them into the air. Well, if he'd let one of those balls slip, or if he'd got cut or jagged at all, he was finished. But he was standing and throwing them up – he was even catching them in his teeth, you see! So the old man looks, and he says: "Look at that ship just coming in," he says, "and there's a man on it," he says, "he's some kind of King by his wearing apparel," he says. "I can see medals and things glittering in the sun on his chest" – you see.

So the boy looks, and he says, "So it is!" – And the old woman, she was out with them.

But this boat came in fairly close, and they lowered a small boat, and this man came in. And he came up to the old man, and said: "It's a fine day, my old man," he said. And he asked, "What are you doing?"

And the old man told him he was a fisher, and told him what he did for a living.

And he said, "That's fine." And he said, "That's a rare-looking boy you've got there," he said, "a fine strapping lad, to help you."

"Oh," says the old man, "yes," he says, "he's a fine lad, he's the only one we've got."

So they started talking about the boy, and the King says – (this was a King, but the old man didn't know that at the time) – he says to the old man: "I'll tell you," he says to the old man, "if you could give me your son for one year and a day," he says, "I'd make a very clever man out of him."

So the old man says, "Oh," he says, "I couldn't say anything about that; you would have to see the old wife," he says, "because," he says, "if I was to take it into my own hands to give you my son, and anything happened to him," he says, "I wouldn't take the responsibility. You'll have to see her yourself."

So this King, he shouts to the old woman to come down, and between her and the old man – the King coaxing them, and saying that he'd make a man of him, and see him in a good position, and one thing and another – the old woman agreed to give him the boy for the year and the day.

She says, "There's nothing here for the boy barring mending the nets, and the old man could nearly do that himself."

So the King gets this boy.

So the two of them go out to the ship, and the ship turns and sails away. So the old man, he goes on from day to day, just catching his fish and taking them in, and mending his nets, and looking after the house, and one thing and another, like that: till the year and the day roll by, and he's out very early in the morning down at the water, watching for this boat.

But by about ten o'clock, he sees the sails coming over the horizon of the sea. And this is this full-rigged ship coming. And when it came in closer, the old man saw his son standing on the bridge, and he's flinging *seven* poison balls up, and catching them in his teeth, and doing great tricks.

So the old man's delighted, and he runs up for the old wife. "Come on down," he says, "the ship's in," he says, "and I see our son on the bridge, and the King's standing beside him, and he's flinging seven poison balls up into the air. The King must have taken a great interest in him," he says, "to teach him to juggle with seven poison balls."

So the King came in in a little boat, and the boy was glad to get home, you see, and cuddled his mother, and shook hands with his father, and they all went up into the little house. They hadn't very much to give him in those days – perhaps a bit of barley bannock, and a drink of milk and some fish, or something like that. But they got whatever was going.

So the old wife was well pleased with the boy. And the King says, "Mistress," he says, "if you could give me him for *another* year and a day, I'd make him twice as good."

So, glad enough to see her boy getting on, she consented for the next year and a day – you see?

So away the ship goes with the boy again – and the old man, he's just at his work as usual – till the next year and a day rolls by. And he's down at the beach as usual, standing at the boat, and continually glancing out to see if the boat was coming. But he stood all day, and there was no sign of the ship; nor was there the next day, nor the day after that. He could have stood there for another year and never clapped eyes on the boat.

Well, when he went up, she pitched into him, and she hit him over the head with the poker, and she gave him the wildest drubbing with sticks – would have nothing to do with him at all, until he undertook to go and get her son back.

So he has to go. He pulled his boat up from the water, and rolled his nets up and stowed them away in a dry place in the shed. And she baked him a barley bannock, and a pancake of some kind, and she rolled them up for him, and stuck them into his hand.

"Now," she says, "you'll go," she says, "and you'll get my son."

So the old man went off – he didn't know which way to go. But he just marched straight on – on, and on, and on – there was sheep fanks, bullock-fanks and all the fanks of Tara – till he came to a great forest. And he's going through the forest and through the forest, and he comes to a little house: and there's an old, old, old man in this little house. And he goes up, and he knocks at the door. This old man comes out, and he says: "It's a rare day," he says, "my man."

"Yes, old man, it is a rare day, sir," he says. "But I'm not enjoying it at all," he says, "because I'm not feeling very well after long walks," he says, "and I haven't had much sleep."

"Oh," says this old man, "come in and I'll give you something to eat," he says, "and a night's shelter. And you can freshen yourself up for your morning walk, wherever you're going."

So he went in, and he got something to eat from this old man, sitting at the fire and talking away, and the old man says: "Where are you going?" he says.

"To tell you the truth, I'm looking for my son," he says. "He was taken away in a ship. I don't know what the man was or what he wasn't, but he was a very clever man. And he was to make a real gentleman and a clever man out of my son," he says. "But," he says, "the first year he came back right enough: but the second year he put in no appearance at all. And," he says, "I must search for him."

"Well," he says, "I can't tell you much about it," he says, "but it looks to me as if the King of the Black Art has got your son. But I can't tell you where he is, or where you can find him. But," he says, "you can keep on – maybe a week's travelling – and you'll come to an older brother of mine, and he'll be able to tell you more about it than I can."

So in the morning the old man gets some bread from the other old man to take with him on his journey; he spits on his stick, and away he goes. And he's on, and on, and on, for another full week he travels on, until he comes to another little house, and he knocks at the door. And out comes another old man. Well, if the first old man was old, this other one was *three times* as old. He was very nearly rockin' on his two front teeth – you see?

So the old man says: "Come in," he says, "my man, you look weary and tired," he says, "and it's looking like rain," he says, "it's not a night for a dog to be out. Come in," he says, "and get what's going."

So in he goes, and he tells him about being at his brother's place, and tells him about his son.

"Well," says this old man, "you'll have a job getting him. Because the King of the Black Art rules all this country – this countryside here – he and his two sons. And," he says, "you'll be very very lucky if you get him back. But I'll tell you what to do when you get up in the morning. If you keep straight on through the wood," he says, "you'll come to the castle. And," he says, "when you go up and ring the bell, and he comes out, you'll ask about your son. And," he says, "they'll laugh at you," he says. "And you'll go in, and he'll fetch fourteen pigeons out, and there will be seven strung on his arm, from there to there. And he'll throw them up in the air, and he'll tell you to pick your son out from among them. And the one you'll pick," he says, "will be the little ragged looking one at the bottom," he says, "pick that one. But," he says, "don't mention you were here, don't mention my name at all," he says.

So all well and good, the old man went to his bed, and he couldn't get up quick enough in the morning to get up to the castle – you see?

So he goes up, anyway, to the castle – it would be about a couple of hours' walk from this old man's hut in the wood to the castle – and he rings the bell.

Out come two men with swords – you know what I mean – old-fashioned soldiers.

"What do you want?"

"I want to see the King," he says.

"Oh," he says, "you can't see the King," he says, "get out of here, you tramp," he says, "or I'll put your head on the poisoned spears."

"Ho ho," says the old man, "you'll not do that," he says. "You go in and tell the King that the old fisherman wants to see him."

So one of the soldiers goes away in and tells the King. The King comes striding out.

"Hullo," he says, "my old man," he says, "what are you after?"

"I'm after my son," he says, "and if I don't get him, I'll make the highest stone in your castle the lowest inside two minutes."

"Oho," says the King, "I'll give you your son," he says. "Wait there a minute or two."

So in he goes, and he comes out with the fourteen pigeons, and he flings them up into the air.

"Now pick your son out of these," he says.

So the old man looks.

"Well," he says, "I'll take that one," he says, "fluttering at the bottom – that ragged-looking one."

"Well," he says, "take him, and be damned to you."

And, just like that, the son was at the father's feet. And the two of them turn and walk away, you see – down this path, away.

The son says, "It's a good thing you came for me, because I would never have got away," he says. "There's the King and his two sons," he says, "and they do all the black magic, all the black art in the country. And," he says, "I've learned a good lot from him. And I'll tell you," he says, "when we're going back this way to our house, I'll tell you how we can get some money, going back the road," he says, "to keep the old woman at home. Now," he says, "in this first village there's a fair tomorrow, and on the road going into the fair," he says, "I'll turn myself into a greyhound dog, one of the loveliest dogs that you ever saw. And," he says, "I'll be sporting and jumping, and jumping over the confectionery stalls, and jumping over the horses' backs, and everybody will be wanting to buy me. But," he says, "don't sell me," he says, "until the King of the Black Art comes to you – he and his two sons. And he'll offer you five hundred pounds for me. Well," he says, "take his five hundred pounds, but," he says, "don't on the peril of your life sell the belt that's on my neck. Before you give me to him," he says, "take the belt off my neck."

The father says, "All right," he says, "I'll do that."

So, the next morning they come up to the village – this village where the fair was; the son turns himself into a big brindled hound – O, the loveliest looking you ever saw! And it's jumping, and it's galloping, and it's springing over the confectionery stalls, jumping over the horses' backs – and all the great gentlemen – in those days, you know, they liked greyhound dogs, and hunting falcons, you see? And the nobility loved a good dog, you see?

So every gentleman that sees him, "Will you sell the dog? Will you sell the dog?"

So the King of the Black Art comes.

"Will you sell the dog, my man?"

"No," he says, "you wouldn't give me enough for him."

"I'll give you five hundred guineas for him," he says.

"All right," says the old man, "he's yours – but I'm not sellin' the belt that's on his neck."

He takes the belt from the dog's neck, and puts a string round it, and hands him over with the string round his neck, you see? And he gets the five hundred guineas, and the old man walks out of the village – and just like that, the son's walking just behind him.

The son was the belt – you see?

So they go on their way, and reach the next town.

"Now," the son says, "father," he says, "the fair will be held in the town tomorrow. And," he says, "When we get to the next town, I'll turn

127

myself into a stallion pony. And I'll be jumping, and kicking, and stepping up and down that street," he says, "the like of it you've never seen. And the same procedure will happen again," he says, "everyone will be wanting to buy me. But don't sell me," he says, "till the King of the Black Art comes, he's the one with the most money. And," he says, "when you sell me to him," he says, "don't sell the bridle that's on the horse's head, or I'm undone."

So the next day, they're coming in this town, you could see the cattle and the old men, and their goats and beasts, going to the fair – you know – to get started. And this young lad, he turns himself into a stallion pony, and it's jumping, and it's kicking, and it's rearing, and – O, it's the loveliest pony you ever saw. Everybody's admiring him going up the street. Two or three men try to buy him, but no, the old man hangs on until the King of the Black Art comes.

"How much do you want for your pony, my old man?" he says.

"Well," he says, "I wouldn't like to sell him," he says.

"I'll give you a thousand pound for him," he says.

"No," says the old man, "I wouldn't like to take a thousand pound for him."

"I'll tell you what I'll do," he says. "I'll give you two thousand pound for him," he says, "if you let me get one try on his back."

"No," says the old man, "I wouldn't let you do that."

"Well," he says, "I'll tell you, come here till you see this." And he takes the old man – the old man has the horse by the head, you see – he takes him over, and he opens the door of a shed – like a stable-place – and he shows the old man, and he says:

"Do you see that heap of gold sovereigns there?"

The old man looks over – I guarantee there was a heap of sovereigns about two feet off the ground – you see? He says:

"I'll give you that heap of gold sovereigns for your pony," he says, "but I would have to get a small run round on his back – a short run round on his back," he says, "for you can't buy a pig in a poke. If you can allow me that," he says, "I'll give you all the gold that's lying there."

Well, the greed was in the old man – you see what I mean?

"Well," he says, "I can't think a ride around the place where the tents are on the fair-ground would do much harm."

So he says, "All right."

The King takes the horse's reins, jumps on its back and goes galloping away, and the old man turns to look at the gold, and it's nothing but horse-dung! A heap of horse-dung – you see? And the horse is away, son and all – you see?

Well, the old man's afraid to go home. He wandered about, and he lay in the woods. He wouldn't go home.

But we'll leave the old man now, and we'll go back to the King's castle.

They take the son, and they keep him in the form of the horse, and they put him into a nine-stalled stable, with other horses. And the food he got was three buckets of salt and beef a day, and not a drink of water, till the horse's tongue was stiff and thick, and coated with a white crust – you know what I mean, with the want of water.

But one day he was standing in the stable, in the shape of the horse, till he looks around and he sees the stable-boy coming in, you see, with the bucket of salt beef, and he says to the stable-boy:

"Listen, stable-boy."

"What is it?" says the stable-boy.

He says: "You wouldn't," he says, "give me one drink of water?"

The stable-boy says: "Look," he says, "you know I can't give you water, because if I give you water, my head will be on the poison spears before the sun sets."

"Well, God bless me, would you not give me one drop?" he says. "No-body'll know, they're away out today on the hill shooting, there's not one of them about the castle. If you could even take me," he says, "by the reins to the water, I'd get so much at a single gulp that you wouldn't need to do it again."

Well, the boy looked all round about – you know.

"Well," he says, "I'll take you to the stream, but I'll never take you there a second time," he says. "I'll give you one drink, and one drink only."

"Well," says the son, "that'll be enough."

So the boy loosens the reins, and takes the horse to the water, and he tried to get a drink. And he says to the stable-boy, "Look," he says, "I can't get a proper drink because of the bit in my mouth. Couldn't you take the bit out?" he says, "and loosen this choke-strap, so that I can get a *proper* drink while I'm at it."

So the boy loosens the choke-strap, and slips out the bit – and as soon as this was done, he just did *That* with his head, and he was out of the bridle, and away as a salmon in the stream. And all the bells of the castle started to ring! The noise that came from the castle, you could have heard it about ten miles away.

11

So the King and his two sons, they're away out on the hill shooting and they hear the commotion – you see? And they're back down, as fast as they could come. And when they found out that he was away as a salmon in the water, the King and his two sons, they changed themselves into three otters, and they're into the river, and they're after him. And they're down the river, and down the river, and down the river, and down the river, till they started to gain on him. They're gaining on him till there wasn't the breadth of this house between them, these three otters and the fish. Till this Jack – they called the son Jack – he turned himself into a swallow in the air – and he's away as a swallow – you know. And these three otters, they turn themselves into three hawks, and they're after the swallow. And they're diving, and skidding, and dipping and swooping over woods and valleys, till they come to the outskirts of a village. And as the swallow's diving – you know the way swallows dive over the ground – he looks into this garden in front of this little house, where there was a lady sitting knitting – and this Jack, he turns himself into a ring on the lady's finger – you see?

Well, they couldn't very well turn into their own shapes, and come and take the ring off the lady, or there would have been a commotion – you see what I mean? They turn themselves into labourers. But before they come up to her, Jacks speaks to the lady – you see – as the ring. But she's looking for the voice, and he explained to her not to be frightened – you see? And in those days people weren't frightened at anything like that, because witchcraft was plentiful. You see what I mean – things like that were supposed to happen.

"Now," he says, "lady, you'll be getting a visit from three labourers, and they'll be offering to do small jobs – jobbing labourers," he says, "they'll call at your door. And," he says, "they'll do a job for you – your wall is needing repairing: I know. And when they get the job done," he says, "they're not to get any payment bar the ring that's on your finger. And before you give them the ring off your finger," he says, "you must collect all those branches and sticks that are lying at the back of your house," he says, "and make a great big bonfire of them, with tar, and any kind of burning material to get the fire started. They'll blaze up," he says, "because they're dry. And," he says, "when they do the job for you, before you give me to them, just turn round and tell them you'd rather throw me in the fire, and fling me right into the centre of the fire."

So she promised she would do it. So she's just sitting there, maybe about another half-hour or so in the sun, when up come these three jobbing labourers, looking for a job.

130

"Well," she says, "I've got a job I need done – my walls. Do you make a good job?"

"Yes," they say, "we make a good job – very cheap."

Well, they did this repair for the lady, and O, they made a lovely job of the wall, in a very short time.

So she asked them how much the job came to.

"Well," he says, "we don't take any money," he says, "we'll let you off with the money part of it," he says, "if you could give us that ring that's on your finger."

"O," she says, "you can't have that," she says. "Before I gave you that, I'd rather fling it into that fire."

And she flung the ring right into the middle of the fire.

Well, at the back of the fire, there was about half a ton of barley, in bags – you see? Sitting up against a shed where they'd been thrashing.

The three labourers, they turned themselves into three blacksmiths with bellows. And they blew the fire, and they blew the fire, and they blew the fire, and they blew the fire, and they blew the fire, till the sparks and the flames were flying everywhere, until there was nothing left of the sticks but a handful of red-ends – you know what I mean, just a small heap of red-ends. And they were blowing and blowing.

Jack, he turned himself into a grain of corn in one of the sacks. So they turned themselves into three cocks, and they're picking, and picking, and picking, and picking, and picking, and picking at this barley, till, when they had just about six or seven seeds to go, Jack turned himself into a fox – very, very sharp! – and nipped the three heads off them with his teeth.

And that finished the King of the Black Art. Jack, he goes and he collects his father on the road, and goes home to the old wife, and they lived happy ever after. They moved into a great big castle, with the money that Jack earned after that. And the last time I was there, I was at the back door, and I got my tea off a little thin table – and the table bended – and my story's ended!

## FARQUHAR, SON OF ALASDAIR

It was MacVurich who was foster-father to Anna, the daughter of MacDonald of Clanranald, and she had been reared in MacVurich's own house in Staoiligearraidh from her childhood until she became a

11·

131

woman. Then, one day, she mentioned that while she had been asleep she had had a dream.

"Well now," said her foster-father to her, "what was the dream that you saw?"

"I dreamt that a cuckoo had shit on me," she replied.

"O, well," said her foster-father to her, "you are not to be in Mac-Vurich's house when that happens!"

What he did was to apportion her dowry to her immediately – seventeen cows and a bull – and off he went home with her to Ormicleit, to her father, driving the cattle before them.

From the castle in Ormicleit they observed the herd of cattle that approached on the white sands with a man and a woman following them. When they came nearer, those in the castle recognized who they were. "King of the Universe!" said MacDonald, "what has Anna my daughter done to her foster-father that he and she are coming here and her dowry with her?"

Anyway, when MacVurich and his foster-child arrived at Ormicleit, MacDonald asked what Anna had done wrong. MacVurich replied that the girl had done nothing wrong, but that she herself wished to return home.

Now in those days they had a custom in Uist of holding a communal gathering at the end of harvest; in this very year they had a gathering in Ormicleit when the crops had been brought home.

That evening, as time wore on, it seemed as if the supply of liquor had become somewhat small for the company, and the Lady of Clanranald sent the girl Anna out of the house where the festivities were being held to the Big House to fetch more liquor. When the girl came back inside with the liquor she showed signs of weeping. Her mother asked her what was wrong with her. The girl replied that after she went outside she had fallen on a heap of shells and had cut her knee.

"Oh, indeed," said her mother, "I knew from the look in the eye of Farquhar son of Alasdair that he was plotting something." And she observed what night it was and bore it in mind.

Nine months from that night MacDonald of Clanranald's daughter had a baby boy, and she named Farquhar son of Alasdair, the grieve, as his father. There was nothing for it then but to seize him and cast him handcuffed into a stronghold.

So there was Farquhar son of Alasdair in prison. A man brought food to him regularly, and one day the prisoner asked this man to leave the prison door open when he left that night. This the man did, and that night the prisoner got away. He set off and reached the gate at the boundary of Staoinibrig where he began to rub his handcuffs against the gate until he loosened the bolt that secured them. This was known because the bolt was found beside the gate a little while afterwards.

The prisoner set off in the direction of the moor, and he arrived at Hann Bay at the end of Loch Aoineart, knowing that there he would find a boat to take him to the mainland. He went to the house of the man who lived at Hann, and he was very well treated there: the people of the house realized perfectly who he was and that he was on the run. Food was brought to him at the table, and he and the man of the house and his wife chatted together while they ate. Then the man of the house got up and went outside. Farquhar son of Alasdair, who remained inside at his meal, began to get restive when the other did not return; and, because he was suspicious of him, he himself rose up and went out and made his way down to the shore. He had a look at the skiff, and a stone had been cast through her bottom. In a flash he realised how things stood, that it was the man of the house who had done this, and that he was now on the way to Ormicleit to betray him. Off he went in the direction of the homestead (Ormicleit) following the man who had gone. Some little distance on the way inland he caught up with him and he killed him on the spot. Then he threw his body into a nearby river, and that body was not discovered until the following year when the bones were found in the river. The river is called the River of the Bones to this day.

Thereupon the prisoner returned to Hann. He found a turf-cutter and cut a sod of heath and placed it on the floor boards of the skiff over the hole. Underneath he put some kind of caulking, and off he went with her. It was learnt afterwards that he reached the mainland safely.

Well, in Uist the son grew up to be a big stalwart man; Ranald was his name. When he came to manhood, his grandfather gave him Staoinibrig and this made him a landed laird. Shortly after this, a boat carrying a cargo of liquor came to the ford and people were unloading hogsheads and putting them into a storehouse on the jetty. Then a wager was laid that anyone who got a hogshead up the stairs with his head and without touching it with his hands, would receive the hogshead as his own. There were many who wanted to try but lacked courage; but then Ranald, MacDonald of Clanranald's daughter's son, tried. He went off with the hogshead and pushed it up the stairs with the strength of his head; but, through some mischance or other, his foot slipped and the hogshead came down and crushed his head.

Ranald was greatly missed and it was now that there occurred to his relatives certain words that an old man who lived in the neighbourhood had uttered one day when he was in MacDonald of Clanranald's house and Ranald was a little child in the cradle. The old man had stood over the child looking at it. He put his hand on its head and said, "Cruel, cruel to me is the suffering that will come upon that little fair head yet!"

"What is the suffering that you see coming to the child?" asked MacDonald of Clanranald.

"Oh, it's nothing," said the old man. "I am sure that neither you nor I shall live to see the thing happen."

It was when Ranald was killed that the prophecy made for him as a little child came to people's minds, and a plaintive, sad song was composed to him after his death.

# IRELAND

## CLUASACH AND THE SEA-WOMAN

There was a man long ago called An Ceannaí Fionn, the Fair-haired Merchant. He was a very sharp and clever fellow who knew the reason for everything, three things only excepted, and about them he could never find out anything at all – the length of an Autumn night, the mind of women, and where the horizon ends. So he and a friend named Cluasach decided to get a ship and to sail off to sea to find the place where the horizon ended. They provisioned their ship for thrice seven years. They were seven years going, seven coming back, and seven years sailing here and there. They continued their course until the vessel's prow got stuck in a wood they met with on the sea, and they could go no further. They tied their ship to a tree, and they put the tying of a day and full year upon her, even tho' they might be absent from her for an hour only, and they laid up the boat in a place where she need not fear that a wave would strike her nor the wind rock her, the sun split her timbers, nor the corner boys throw stones at her. They were journeying then until they met the wall of brass which rose up out of the sea, and neither could get up on the wall, and so they said to each other that it was probable that it was the end of the horizon they had reached when they could go no further.

Well, they turned their ship and made for home. They were coming then until they came to the western side of the Sceilg Rocks, and there they decided to stop for a little, for they were tired, and they wanted to eat a bit and sleep a spell. They threw out an anchor, and ate and slept for a good while. But when they wanted to go they could not hoist the anchor, so they cast lots to see which of them would go down to release it. The lot fell on Cluasach, and he went down to the bottom of the sea, and it is how he found the anchor and it stuck in the threshold of a door in the land of Youth; and beside the door was a young girl combing her hair into a golden basin with a comb of silver, and she was resting the sole of her foot on the anchor. Cluasach said to her that she should have let them pull up the anchor, and not to have given him the trouble of coming down. But she said that it was not the anchor that she wanted but himself. He said that he would not stay, and for her to let the anchor go and let them pull it up. She would not promise him that but said that he would have to stay, and the man above could pull up the anchor. He promised to return for her, but said that they had been voyaging for many years, and that his people at home would be uneasy, and he must return to give them his tidings. So she let him go.

When Cluasach returned to his comrade they hoisted all the sails they had and sailed for home. Cluasach was looking after the sails and his companion was at the rudder. Cluasach saw a huge wave rising in their wake, and making towards them at great speed. In the immense hollow of the wave, below its crested top, they saw a woman. So Cluasach reached for his bow and shot an arrow at the woman in the wave, and it took the eye out of her head; and thereupon the wave disappeared.

Soon they saw a horseman coming towards them riding on the top of the water on a slender brown horse and as they were approaching Ceann Bóluis he caught up with them. He said that it was better for Cluasach to have married his sister when she had two eyes in her head than to marry her now when she had only one. Cluasach promised to marry her, but asked that they should be allowed to go home to tell of his adventures to his friends and neighbours, and that they would come to him on any day he appointed. And so he left them, having fixed a day, and the two men returned to their homes. When the day came, Cluasach was accompanied to the shore by his friends and he promised them to send a sign that he lived every May morning, and the sign would be a sod of turf which had been partly burned. His friends then stood and watched while he walked down to a rock on the edge of the sea, and then there came a mighty wave which covered him and the rock, and he was seen no more.

The turf sods came year after year on each May morning for a long time. I never saw them myself, but I saw the man who saw them.


## THE WOMAN WHO WENT TO HELL

There was a widow there long ago, as there often was and will be again. She had only the one daughter, and her name was Máire. The daughter took the notion to marry, any way, and the man she married was Mící na Muc. They weren't long married when Mící wanted to banish the poor old widow from the house. She asked him for time to spin seven pounds of wool and she got it. Seven years went by before she had them spun. Micí said that her time was well up now and he ordered her to leave the following day. She said she would. The following morning, she took the daughter with her, and off with them; they travelled the road until they came to a farmer's house. They asked for lodgings and got them. During the night, the young woman asked what kind of a house that was, further up on the farm.

"Would you go to mind it tonight?" asked the man of the house.

"I would," said Máire.

"I will give you twenty pounds, if you stay in it till the morning," says the farmer.

"I'll go there, if you take good care of my mother," said Máire.

"There's no fear but she will get good care," said the man of the house.

Máire set out and went into the house. She kindled a fire and swept the floor; then she sat on the chair and drew out a book. She started to read it. It wasn't long until a woman, with a spancel and a milk-can, walked up the floor towards her, and a cow out in front of her. She ordered Máire to get up and to milk the cow. Máire got up and milked the cow. The woman told her to take three drinks of the milk, to wash her hands and face in the remainder, and to throw it against the wind. Máire did as she was told. The woman went off, and Máire sat down again. No sooner had the woman gone than a strapping man walked up the floor to Máire, and he grimacing fiercely at her. He sat down by her side and remained there until the cock crowed. He went off then. As soon as Máire had the daylight in the morning, she left the house and made off to the farmer's, and the first thing she did was to ask how her mother was. The mother said she was all right herself, if Máire was too.

"I am," said Máire.

She started to work, and pretended nothing about this or that until the night came. The farmer asked her would she go there again that night. She said that she would, if her mother got good care. The farmer said that he would give her forty pounds for going that night. When night came, she made off to the house and went in. She kindled the fire, swept the floor and lighted a candle. She sat down and pulled a book to her and started to read it. It wasn't long until the woman came to her, with a spancel and a milk-can, and the cow out in front of her. She ordered Máire to rise and milk the cow. Máire stood up and milked the cow.

"Take three drinks of the first of the milk," said the woman. "Wash your hands and your face in the remainder of it, and throw it against the wind."

Máire did as she was ordered. The woman then left her, and she

137

was barely gone when the man came to her; as bad as he was the first night, his appearance this night was seven times worse. He sat on a chair in front of Máire, but she didn't pretend to see him until the cock crowed. He went off then. As soon as Máire saw the daylight, she left and made off to the farmer's house. The first word she asked was how her mother was, and the mother said she was all right, if Máire was. Máire said she was. She kept at her work until night came. The farmer asked her would she go again that night. She said she would, if her mother was cared for, and the farmer said she would be, and welcome.

"And you will get sixty pounds, if you go there tonight," said he.

She left when the night came, and went to the house. She lighted a candle, swept down the floor and sat her on her chair reading her book. She wasn't long there when the woman came to her, with her spancel and milk-can, and the cow out in front of her. She told Máire to rise and milk the cow. Máire got up and milked her.

"Take three drinks of the first of the milk now," said the woman. "Wash your hands and face in the rest of it and throw it against the wind."

Máire did as she was told.

"Now," said the woman of the cow, "he will come to you again tonight and, as bad as he was for the past two nights, he will look seven times more terrible tonight. He will say that he will eat you alive tonight. You are to tell him that he won't, because there is a good guard between you and him."

The woman went away, and Máire sat down in the same place reading her book. She wasn't long seated when the man came up along the floor towards her, and whatever way he looked the previous nights, he looked worse still this night. He sat on the chair, and he wasn't long there when he spoke:

"I'll eat you alive tonight, Máire," said he.

"Ah, you won't," said Máire, "because there's a good guard between me and you."

"I wouldn't doubt you, Máire!" said he.

"What damned you, you devil?" said Máire.

"I'll tell you," said he. "When this house was being built, my father appointed me as steward over the men, and then when they had their money earned, I kept it from them. That damned me. And now," said he, "when you go back to my father, he will be ready to pay you. Don't take a penny from him, but ask him instead to let you sleep in a certain room in his house. He will agree to that, and welcome, although my mother won't like it."

She went to the farmer's house, and as soon as she went in, she asked how her mother was. The mother said she was all right, if Máire was.

"I am all right," said Máire.

She settled in to work and pretended nothing. The people of the house were surprised that she wasn't saying anything. At dinner-time, the man of the house went to her to pay her, and she said she wouldn't take any penny from him, but to give her the certain room to sleep in. The farmer said she would get it, and welcome.

"It is my child's room?" said the old woman in the corner. "She won't get it!"

"She will get it," said the farmer. "'Tis a lot of money."

She was given the room to sleep in, and she slept in it for some time. Then a day or two came when she didn't get up of bed at all, and the woman of the house was blaming her. The woman told one of the servants to go and peep in through the key-hole. She did so, and what did she see but Máire with a baby in her arms and a strapping man sitting in her company at the bedside. She ran down and told the woman.

"'Tis true after all!" said the farmer's wife. "Máire is holy and I am damned. That's my son with her. Go up to her now," said she, "and tell her that we want to put certain things into her room, to hide them, fearing anybody would take them."

The servant girl went and asked the woman in the bed would she let the things into her room. Máire said she would. They bundled the farmer's wife up in every kind of way, and carried her into the room. During the night – she wasn't long in the room at all – she saw her son coming, and he sat down beside the bed where Máire had the child. His mother lost patience, and she threw off whatever clothes were on top of her, and caught hold of her son.

"May God help us now, mother!" said he. "If you had waited two more hours, you would have had me for ever. Now, I'll have to spend seven years in Hell because of you!"

"You won't, my love," said the mother, "because I'll go there myself in your stead."

"You won't, mother, for you couldn't do it," said the son.

"I will," said she.

Off she went to Hell to spend seven years there in her son's stead, and if she did, it wasn't long until she returned, and she burned and scorched!

"I knew that you couldn't do it," said the son.

"I'll go," said his father.

"You won't, for you couldn't," said the son.

The father set off, but he didn't go even as far as the mother and he returned.

"I'll go there," said Máire, "if you take good care of my mother until I come back."

"You'll do it all right," said the son.

He gave Máire a ring and told her not to eat any bite of food she got in Hell, but to give it to a dog that was lying across the threshold of Hell. The food would come to her through the ring. That's what happened. She went to Hell and finished her seven years there; and she gave all the food that was given to her to the dog, Caesar, that was lying across the door. When the seven years were up, she asked the Devil for her wages. He replied that she had eaten the value of her wages. Máire replied that she had eaten no food, that she had given it all to Caesar. Caesar was asked had he been getting her food and he said he had. The Devil then asked her to spend seven years more there, and she agreed. She spent the second seven years there, and when they were up, she asked for her wages. The Devil said she had eaten the value of her wages. She said that he should ask Caesar, and Caesar said that he himself had eaten the food. She was then asked what wages she wanted. She asked for all the souls which were suffering most in Hell, that they be put up on her back. The souls were put up on her back, as many as she could carry, and she went out the door of Hell with them. Whom should she meet coming in the gate of Hell but Micí na Muc, the man she was married to long ago!

"Will you take me with you, Máire?" he asked.

"I don't know," said she. "Still, 'tis said that one should return good for evil. Get up on my back, if you can find room!"

Off she went, and it wasn't long until she met a gentleman.

"That's a heavy load you have, my girl," said he.

"'Tis," said Máire. "I'll try to carry it, anyway."

"Would you sell them?" he asked.

"I would," she replied. "But who are you?"

"I am Saint John," he replied.

"I won't sell them to you at all," said Máire, "because I earned them more dearly than you did!"

She continued on her way and soon she met a second man.

"That's a heavy load you have, my girl," said he.

"'Tis," said Máire. "I'll try to carry it, anyway."

"Would you sell them?" he asked.

"I would," said she. "But who are you?"

140

"I am Saint Michael," said he.

"I wouldn't sell them to you at all," said Máire, "because I earned them more dearly than you did!"

She continued on her way, and it wasn't too long until she met a third man. He and Máire saluted each other.

"You have a heavy load, Máire," said he.

"I have," said she.

"Would you sell them?" he asked.

"I would," said Máire, "but who are you?"

"I am the Saviour," said he.

"I'll sell them to you," said Máire, "because, as dearly as I earned them, you earned them even more dearly!"

She gave him the souls, and they went up to Heaven in the shape of bright doves. She continued on her way then along the road until the dew and the lateness of the night came on her. She met a poor man, and she asked him where he was going to spend the night.

"I'm going to a wedding-feast in a house above here," he replied. "A man who has been a widower for fourteen years is getting married again."

"All right," said Máire. "I'll go along with you."

They went up to the house and entered. They seated themselves inside the door. A stripling youth came and stood in front of Máire, putting his two eyes through her. Máire had a notion that she recognized him as the son whom she had left behind her when she went to Hell. He stood there putting his two eyes through her. Máire asked him why he was taking more notice of her than of anyone else.

"It would be more fitting," said she, "that you'd go and tell your father that there's a poor woman here, and that he should give her something to eat!"

The boy went off and told his father, and, faith if he did, back he came with a dish of meat. Máire and the poor man ate their fill. When they were drinking whatever kind of drink they were given, Máire asked the poor man to leave some drink in the bottom of his drinking-vessel. He did so. Máire pulled the ring off her finger – the ring that she got from the man who was going to Hell – and she threw it into the vessel and gave it to the boy.

"Here," said she, "take that to your father now, and tell him to drink that in memory of your mother."

The boy took the vessel to his father and told him what the poor woman had said. He drank the drink, and when he did, he felt the ring in his mouth. He recognized it well, for his name and surname were on it.

141

"Take me to that poor woman, my boy," said he.

"I will," said the boy.

He took his father by the hand and pulled him through the crowd until he came in front of Máire. The father stretched out his hand and gave her a hundred thousand welcomes. He said he thought that she had failed to keep her word and that she was dead and buried long since. He took her with him and dressed her up in fine clothes – she must have needed them after fourteen years! He told the others to go off home, and that he would pay the expenses of the wedding-feast himself.

"My first wife has come back to me," said he, "and she is the only wife I will have. It is she who bought me dearly."

He married Máire, and they lived in health and plenty from that on.

That's my story, and if 'tis a lie, let it be!

## THE SON OF THE KING OF THE SPECKLED MOUNTAIN

There was a King in Ireland long ago. He had one son, and he sent him to school to Manannán. He spent seven years with him, and after the seven years he left him with him for seven years more. When the fourteen years were up he left him with him for another seven, that was a year and twenty. When he had taught him for twenty-one years, he (the King's son) asked Manannán: "Well now," says he, "is there under the world today any man that is more skilled in feats of activity and of valour than myself?"

"Well, there is not," says the master, "any man today under the world more skilled than you except one man!"

"What is his name?" says the King's son.

"I do not know," says Manannán, "where he hails from nor where he lives, but his name is Mac Dournáin, the son of the King of the Speckled Mountain."

"I put myself under bonds, and under the great sorrow of the year," says the King's son, "not to sleep the second night on the same bed, nor to eat the second meal off the same table, whether he be under the ground or over the ground, until I find him."

He arose on the following morning, he washed his hands, and he said his prayers, and down he went then to the shore of the sea. He took out his pocket knife, took up a piece of a stick, and from it made a ship, big, full and mighty, with no end of feather in nor top of feather out but one feather alone making shelter and fairy music for the whole. He thrust out to sea, and gave prow to sea and stern to shore. He sailed away; and he would not catch up with the March wind that was before him, nor the March wind that was behind him would not catch up with him either. He was sailing and ever sailing until he came in sight of an island. There was a very large gathering of people on the island.

"Perhaps," says he, "this is the place I am seeking!"

He drew in his ship, and he put the tying of seven years upon her, even tho' he might not be longer away from her than a single hour. What did he find there but a young Queen sitting in a chair of gold, and beside her was a chair of silver. Up he goes to her. He asked her what she was doing there. She told him that she was the twelfth daughter of her father. "And," says she, "there is not a year for eleven years that the great giant has not come and carried off one of my sisters. I am the twelfth daughter," says she, "and it was threatened that if my father did not bring me here today the giant would drown the whole island. He wouldn't leave a person at all alive on the island if my father did not put me here today."

Very well. He and she spent a little while talking and conversing with one another, and then he saw a ship, big, full, and mighty, coming towards him; there was the rowing of the hundreds on her and only one person in her. And out of the ship a giant stepped ashore.

"May it be a thousand times worse you may be a year from today!" says the giant. "Only for the excellence of the voyaging I made, my married wife would have been carried off by you!"

"It is not asking for right or justice from you that I came here today," says the King of Ireland's son, "but to take right and justice from you!"

They attacked each other, so that they made hard of the soft, and soft of the hard, until the end of the day and the evening were approaching each other, and the son of the King of Ireland remembered that there was not a man to stretch him nor a woman to lament him. He did nothing but raise his sword and swept the giant's head off.

When the people of the island saw the great giant was dead they scattered in terror and ran for their lives lest the man who had saved the young Queen would drown the island and all that was in it. But he brought her home to her father.

There was a hundred thousand welcomes before him.

"Now," says the father, "since it has happened that you saved her I shall give her to you in marriage, and the half of my kingdom, and the whole of it after my death."

"Well, I am glad to get it," says he. "But," says he, "if I should ever

143

return perhaps I'd make her my wedded wife, and if I don't return may all good chance be hers!"

On the following day he arose, he said his prayers, and he washed his hands, and he struck out along the road. He was going and ever going until the end of the day and evening was approaching, and he saw an island far from him, and not near to him.

"Well," says he, "I'd better go ashore to see if a person at all would have tidings of the place that I am looking for."

He went in there, and he pulled up his ship. He gave the tying of seven years to her, even tho' he might not be there but for an hour only. He was going up through the island, and he saw a house from him, and he went in there. When he went in there was not a person nor a stranger before him. He saw three plates of meat and three bowls of broth laid on the table.

"Goodness knows," says he, "but I'm hungry and it is little that I want," says he, "and it is little that any of these plates will notice my taking a little bite off it, and little will any bowl of broth notice if I take a mouthful out of it."

He took up his knife, and he cut off a piece of the meat from each of the three plates, and he drank three sips from the three bowls of broth. It is not long he was in when he heard a great noise coming. He had no time to go anywhere to hide except on the rails under the table. In came three mighty warriors. They sat down at the table.

"Somebody," says the first, "somebody has cut a bit from my roast of meat!"

"Well," says the second, "he didn't turn his back on my share either."

"Nor did he forget to take his portion from my share also," says the third.

"Somebody took a mouthful out of my bowl of broth," says the first man. "And from mine," says the second. "And from mine," says the third.

They were eating away, and a piece of meat fell from them on to the floor. One of the warriors stooped to pick it up, and what should he see but the son of the King of Ireland underneath, on the rails of the table.

"Hoho!" says he, "who are you? Get out of that!"

He came out. "Well," says he, "if it's not of my will it's of my unwill I came out! I'm the King of Ireland's son, but who are ye?"

"Well," says they, "it is how we are three brothers. We had one sister, and a giant came out of the Western World, and asked us for our sister, that is seven years ago. We had four islands. Our father and mother

144

died, and then the giant came and said we must give him one of the islands. We did not wish to fall out with our brother-in-law, and for love of being great and friendly with him we gave him one of the islands. He came the second year, and he asked the second island of us. There was no desire on us to give it to him, but all the same, sooner than fall out with our brother-in-law – we didn't want to quarrel with him – we gave him the second island. Well now," says he, "he came looking for the third island; and we are at war with him for seven years, and we are as badly off now as ever we were, and we have to fight him and his men every day, and there is no man that we can kill in the day that is not alive again during the night and they all before us ready to fight again the following day."

"Well," says the King of Ireland's son, "maybe I'll give you a hand of help tomorrow."

They spent that night right pleasantly, a third of the night in story-telling, a third in the telling of the high deeds of the Fianna, and a third in deep sleep and slumber, the taste of honey on every bite they ate, and they ate no bite dry, and thus they were until dawn. They went to sleep and in the morning the three warriors arose and took their breakfast; and the King's son was asleep in his bed.

"Bad is this warrior," says one of them, "he hasn't stirred yet out of his bed."

He heard them, and he got up with a leap.

"Is it likely," says he, "that you didn't think it worth while to call me? But maybe I'll be in time enough yet." He got his breakfast and when he had eaten it: "It is not a helping hand," says he, "unless I leave you at rest at home today. What road are you taking?"

"Well, the path is well-trodden by us," says they, "and you will follow it. There are three hills before you. If you get to the second hill you've a third of the journey over, and if you get as far as the third hill you have come two-thirds of the way."

So the King's son set off. He did not stop until he reached the first hill and he sat down there. He saw no appearance of a man or a stranger there, so he said he'd go a bit further. It was the same story with the second hill, but when he came at last to the third hill, he saw below him the speckling of the glens and the darkening of the hills with the multitude of warriors who were making towards him. He went off with himself. He attacked them and fought them until the end of the day when the white horse was going under the shade of the dock-leaf, and not better off was the dock-leaf if she were to wait for her. He remembered that there was

12

no man to stretch him nor woman to lament him. He did not leave a head on body by the time the sun was setting.

"What's the good now," says he, "of going home, since I don't know who these people are nor what is bringing them to life again?"

He lay down until night came. He pulled a corpse under him, a corpse over him, and a corpse on each side of him. He was not long lying there when he saw an old man coming, carrying a pot of healing balm and a little feather. "Get up, lads!" says the old man. He was rubbing the feather to them, and they were rising up into their standing as they were before.

"Don't be in such a hurry, my lad!" says the King's son. "Don't put up any more of them in their standing, for if you do, it is not to me they will be helpful!"

So he out with his sword and stretched them all again, and cut off the head of the old man. He lay back again on the ground and pulled a corpse under him, a corpse over him, and one on each side of him.

When he had that done it was not long until he saw an old white horse coming, carrying a pot of healing balm and a feather. "Up lads," says he, "ye are badly wanted!"

"Not so fast, old white horse," says the son of the King of Ireland. "Put no more of them in their standing, or if you do, it is not me that they will help."

He and the old white horse made at each other, but if they did it is not long the fight lasted.

Down he lay again. But he was not long resting when a huge and terrible hag appeared, carrying a pot of healing balm and a little feather, and she began to put them in their standing.

"Hold a moment, hag," says he, "put no more of them in their standing, or if you do, it is not me that they will help."

"Bad luck to you!" says she, "and no welcome to you, son of the King of Ireland. I'm ready for you. There are nine inches of plate-iron on my neck, nine inches of steel on the nails of my toes, nine inches of steel on my finger-nails, and I have nine feet of a tail of iron to put you to death!"

She twisted the iron tail around him. When she had it twisted around him she began to squeeze him towards her, and when she was squeezing him he thought that his last hour had come. He thrust his arm at her breast and struck his elbow against her, and with the mighty squeezing the hag was giving him he put his elbow right through her, and she died.

He stretched back, and it is he who was tired and weary. He pulled a

146

corpse under him, a corpse over him and a corpse on each side of him. And then he fell into a deep slumber, without stirring or moving. It was not long until one of the big giants came, and with him came his servant, and they had a big turf-basket to hold the dead bodies which they were carrying home to eat. They carried him off with them, and did not stop until they arrived at the giant's castle. The giant and his servant boy started in on the corpses, pulling them from each other and gulping them down.

The next morning when the second giant and his boy were setting off again for the battlefield the old woman, the giant's mother, sat up in bed and shouted to them. "Ah son," says she, "badly did you treat me last night when you came home, and badly did I fare, and if your brother had been here he wouldn't have left me short of food."

"Well, mother," says he, "it was not my turn until today, and had I the chance before this of bringing you anything, in troth, I would not have left you short, here are some corpses left over, and you can be picking at them until I come back tonight, and then I promise you you'll have plenty."

So up gets the old hag, and puts down a great blaze of a fire, she pulls out the bodies from the heap behind her. She began to tear them to pieces and to eat them and she was feeling them one after the other, to choose the best and the plumpest, and she put her hand on the King of Ireland's son, and he is in a deep snoring slumber. She pulls out the fire. "In troth," says she, "if you were roasted at the back of the fire, you would put a little taste on my tongue!" So, when she had the fire red hot, she shoved him into the back of it.

Well, he slept on until the marrow began to boil in his bones, and then he jumped with one clear jump out of the fire and where should he land but behind the old hag on the hob. The hag looked at him! "Musha," says she, "sure it's the Lord sent you, and you're just what I'm looking for to carry in fresh water, and to bring out the turf ashes!"

"Aha, may it be a thousand times worse you'll be a year from now, you old hag!" says the King of Ireland's son, "to have the impertinence in you to think of having me as a lad for water and for turf-ashes," and he struck her a clout and made white-wash of her brains on the kitchen wall. "And I'll do worse than that to you," says he, "for I'll bury you down under the threshold stone where everyone will walk over your carcass as they go out and come in for ever!"

When he had that done, he went out then, and looked around. There was a long street there, and high walls, and lofty houses. He went on

12·

down the street; and he was burned and in rags and sore distress. The eleven daughters of the King of the island were there high up in a sunny bower, and they saw the young man go past below them. The young Princess, the eldest of the girls, looks out and says she:

"The finest man my eyes have ever lighted on is walking down there below, and he is burned and tattered and we have something here to cure him if we could only get him here. Come over here, sisters," says she, "till I cut off your hair, and plait it into a rope so that we may make a ladder of it, and we will bring him in here."

He heard them talking. "Well," says he, "don't cut off your hair, but open the window, and I am no warrior if I am not able to go with a leap in on the window!"

So she opened the window. He arose with a mighty spring, and jumped in on to the floor where they were.

"Now," says she, "there is a barrel of poison here and also a barrel of healing balm, and I don't know one from the other. But wait," says she, "and I'll cut my finger and try which is the right one."

She made a cut in her finger, and which barrel did she put the finger into but the barrel of poison; the pain struck her, so she dipped the finger into the other barrel, and the pain left her.

So the King of Ireland's son went into the barrel of healing balm, and when he was washed and cleaned he was as safe and sound and as good as ever he had been in all his life.

"Well," says the girl, "we are the eleven sisters, the daughters of the King who gave you lodging, and I'm to be married tomorrow to the great giant whose brother you killed yesterday, and my ten sisters will be his mistresses as long as he lives."

Sure enough, next morning a proclamation was made, inviting all on the island to the wedding. The King of Ireland's son went off with himself, and late in the evening he went into a house where an old woman lived who looked after the giant's hens, and he asked for a night's lodging.

"Well," says the hen-wife, says she, "isn't it the great wonder that you are not at the wedding-house?"

"Where's the wedding?" says he.

"O," says she, "and don't you know that the giant and the King's daughter are to be married tomorrow?"

"Indeed," says he, "I never heard a word about it, but perhaps," says he, "that I'm in time enough yet!"

"O, you won't be let in now," says she. "Nobody will be admitted now except a musician or a fool."

148

"Well, I'm not much of a hand at music," says he, "but I'd do right well as a fool."

So he went into the hen-wife's house and when he had got his supper: "Have you a bag?" says he.

"Indeed no, I haven't any bag that's any good."

So he made her fetch him material from the shop, and she brought him twenty-one yards of coarse linen, and thread and needles. When the hen-wife made a stitch he made seventeen stitches, and so between them they made a bag to please him. He went off with himself then, and did not stop until he came to the giant's house. He knocked at the door, and was asked who was there.

"A fool," says he.

"Let him in!"

He was let in, and when he went in the dinner was on the table. Devil a taste on the table that he was not packing into his bag, and when the bag was full, he went to the door and threw it across to the hen-wife's house. He went in then again to the feast, and there was not a taste of what was coming to the table that he did not break or destroy. Everybody began to laugh. The big giant asked them what cause for laughter they had; and one of them said that it was the fool.

"Oh, never mind him," says he, "I'll go down to him and I'll teach him manners."

The young Princesses knew that it was the King of Ireland's son who was doing all this.

But when the big giant came down the King of Ireland's son caught hold of him and tied his hands and feet to each other and threw him into the corner.

"Stay there you now," says he, "till morning!"

Next morning he asked the company what death they preferred him to give to the giant, but they left it to himself, and so he didn't go to any great trouble but just killed him.

Then he appointed the most respectable man he met there as King of the island, and imposed tax and tribute on him, and the following day he sailed away with the King's eleven daughters, and he kept sailing on a steady course for home. He saw an island that he had not noticed the time he was coming already.

"God knows," says he, "but maybe this is really the place I'm looking for."

"If you take my counsel," says the eldest of the King's daughters, "you should not land anywhere but make straight for home!"

149

"Ah," says he, "it's not in my nature nor disposition to return home until I know who is on the island."

So he landed. Who was there but the son of the King of the Turks, with twenty-one of his men, and they looking for pretty women.

When the King of Ireland's son landed on the island, the son of the King of the Turks saw the eleven women who were along with him.

"God's truth," says he, "if ever in my life I saw such fine women as these who are with this man!"

And so he went to his *sean dall glic* – his wise blind counsellor – and asked him to devise some means of putting to death the King of Ireland's son so that he might be able to carry off the women.

"Well," says he, "you have enough to do, for there is no one in the world a match for him. You will never get the upper hand of him unless you make him drunk."

"And how will I make him drunk, can you tell me?" says the son of the King of the Turks.

"I'll tell you that," says the wise man. "Make a hole," says he, "in the floor opposite the place where you're sitting. Get a big funnel and put it inside your shirt up to the throat. Make a bet then with him that there's not a man in the world who can drink as much whiskey as yourself. Well, the Irishman is so stubborn in his inclination and so cross-grained that he will never submit. He'll begin drinking then. Be you then letting the drink down yourself into the funnel, every mortal drop of it, and he'll keep on until he falls down dead drunk."

Well, the two of them had their supper together, the Turk and the King of Ireland's son.

"Now," says the son of the King of the Turks, "I'll lay you a bet and a strong wager that there isn't a man over the ground in the wide world that can drink as much whiskey as myself!"

"I'll take you on," says the King of Ireland's son, "that I'll drink every drop as much as you!"

Well, they started at the drinking and they drank and drank until the King of Ireland's son fell back at last on his chair. Then the other man caught hold of him and tied him with chains firm and fast and threw him into a corner and left him there till morning.

Next day he was for death, and says the young Turk to the King's eleven daughters, "What form of death will I give him now?"

"Well, we don't like him to die at all," says the eldest, "but as it's got to be, throw him over the cliff into the great sea and let him be killed or drown!"

150

"Well, I'll do that!" says he.

He brought him to the edge of the cliff over the sea, and then said the young Queen:

"Now I am asking a request from you. Will you give me permission to give him a kiss before you throw him over?"

"I will," says he.

When she stooped down to kiss him she slipped a magic ring on his finger. He took him then and threw him over the cliff into the sea.

"Now," says the King's daughter, "I put you under bonds and under the great sorrow of the year not to know whether I or my sisters are men or women until the end of a year and a day."

"A good thing is worth waiting for!" says the son of the King of the Turks.

The King of Ireland's son kept going from wave to wave on the top of the sea. Now there's a bird in the sea in those regions, they say, which some call the *Corr* and others the *Griffin*. She has human sense and intelligence. And her nest was up on the side of a cliff, and three young birds in the nest. Well, she saw below her the King of Ireland's son floating on the top of the water, and down she swooped, caught him in her talons and carried him off to her nest. During the day she was always away getting food which she used to feed to her young in the evening. And when she had them fed, she used to give him what was left. But he wasn't satisfied with the slender portion he was getting, and so he killed the young birds one after the other. The griffin said nothing and made no complaint until she came home the third night and found the third fledgling gone with the cliff.

"Well now," says she, "I treated you fairly, but you have left me alone with my birdeens all killed, and so I'll leave you where I found you on the top of the wave."

Well, there he was floating on the sea, and there was no fear of his drowning because of the magic ring on his finger. He was thrown up at last by the sea on a big rock, and there he lay until one day he saw a ship sailing by, and he began to shout and scream. And the captain of the ship heard him.

"Well," says the captain, "there's somebody there on that rock and ye had best go out and see what kind of person it is."

He sent out four of his men in the long boat, but when they saw him, and he so wild looking and covered with hair, they got frightened and returned to the ship. The captain sent out another four.

"Don't come back to me," says he, "unless you bring him with you!"

151

They went off to the rock, and they got frightened, and were coming back again.

The King of Ireland's son was thinking that he would not have another chance, so he pressed his hands and knees together and jumped clean off the rock and into the boat to them, and they landed him on the ship.

"Who are you?" says the captain.

"Well," says the King of Ireland's son, "you are no gentleman nor sea-captain, for if you were you would free me from my bonds."

"That is true," says the captain. The captain then freed him. "Now, who are you?"

"You are no gentleman nor sea-captain, for if you were you would give me food and clothing and put a sword into my hand."

When he had dressed and eaten, he went through all the swords in the ship until he found an old one in the hold, eaten with rust. He shook it, and knocked seven tons of rust off it.

"Now," says he to the captain, "who are ye?"

"Well," says the captain, "I ask pardon and protection from you, it is how I have been looking for a man whose name I do not know, neither do I know under the world where he is. A hero he was, who helped me and my brothers, there is a year and a day ago, he killed all before him and then he left us. But the giant is now in our harbour with a fleet of ships and threatens to take our island from us. And I have come and a lot more with me to seek for the man who helped us before."

"Well," said the King of Ireland's son, "I am that man and I'll help you."

So he returned with the captain to the island where the giant was with his fleet. He sailed into the middle of the ships, and he had a mighty oak club in his hand, and for every blow he struck he sunk a ship, and soon he disposed of the whole of them.

That night he stayed with the captain, but at skreek of dawn on the morrow he was off again on his travels. He didn't stop until he went down to the shore, he pulled out his knife and a piece of stick, cut a skiver off the stick and from it made a ship, great, wide and mighty with no feather in nor no feather out but one feather alone making shelter and fairy music for the whole. He gave bow to the sea and stern to shore, and he never stopped until he struck land and anchorage in the place where he had left the son of the King of the Turks. And there he found that a proclamation had gone out announcing the marriage for the next day. He came to the house of an old woman, and he asked her if she could give him lodging until morning.

"Isn't it a great wonder," says she, "that you're not up at the wedding house?"

"What wedding?" says he.

"The wedding of the son of the King of the Turks and the King's daughter."

"That's the first time I heard about it," says he, "but perhaps I'm still in time to go to the feast."

"No," says the old woman, "for no one will be let in now but a musician or a jester!"

"Well, I'm no good as a musician, but I'd not be too bad as a fool!"

Anyhow off he went to the wedding, and when he said that he was a fool he was let in by the doorkeeper. And then he started, and bad as were his antics and behaviour on the first occasion, he was seven times worse now. The son of the King of the Turks left his place and walked down the room to give him a clout and to put him out the door, but if he did, the King of Ireland's son caught hold of him, tied him with the tying of the five smalls – *ceangal na gcuig gcaol*[1] – and he threw him into the corner and left him there until morning.

And when the dawn came he got four horses and tied him to them, and they made four quarters of the son of the King of the Turks.

He gave the island and all that was in it to the most respectable man he found there, on the condition that he should pay tribute and rent to him during his life. He set off then for home, himself and the King's eleven daughters. As he sailed he came one day close to land, and he saw a man walking on the strand.

"Maybe," says he, "that after all my travels that this is MacDournáin, the son of the King of the Speckled Mountain, the man that I've been looking for!"

"If you take my advice," says the eldest daughter of the King, "you'll stay where you are; you've done enough already."

"Ah," says he, "I cannot stop, and I must go in."

He went ashore and approached the stranger. The man came up to him, and he carrying on his back a huge cauldron.

The two of them attacked each other, and the fight went on for three nights and three days, and on the third day MacDournáin knocked the King's son down on the strand, turned the cauldron on top of him and sat down himself on top of it. And he stayed there sitting on the cauldron, with the King's son underneath, for a whole night and a day. When he

---

1. his neck, his wrists and his ankles fettered together.

thought that he was well smothered, MacDournáin got up and lifted the cauldron, but when he saw that the man he thought dead was still alive he took to his heels across the sands and ran for his life. The King's son shouted after him: "If you are  a real champion you'll come this time to look for me for I won't follow you any more!"

When at length he returned home safe and sound after all his voyaging and adventures there was a hundred thousand welcomes before him, and the King gave him the choice of his daughters.

"I'll marry," says he, "the woman I earned, the woman who saved me, and it's she I'll bring home to the house of my father and mother in Ireland."

He bade farewell to the King and returned home.

When the King of Ireland had his son back again, he prepared a great wedding feast, and he invited all to come, and come they all did. In the middle of the feasting a stranger came to the door. The old King arose and went to the door and asked him to come in.

"I am not going in," says he, "until I find a man who can tell me a story without a lie, and if he does he shall put all kinds of meat – mutton, beef, pork – into my cooking-pot, and when the tale is told without a single lie the meat will be cooked, and I will sit down, and eat my fill of it!"

The old King came back into the parlour where his son and the company were seated, and he gave a sigh which broke one of the rafters in the house.

"You are a man under *geasa,*[2] father," says the King's son.

"O," says the old King, "there's a man outside here, and he put a question on me" – and then he told what happened.

"Wait, father, that's the man for whom I have been seeking. I'll go out to him, and it is short that the tale will be a-telling."

Out went the King's son and they attacked each other. They made hard of soft, and soft of hard, and brought up wells of fresh water thro' the grey slabs of rock. And then the King's son remembered that there was not a man to stretch him nor a woman to lament him. He gave him a twist, and he put him down into the ground to his waist, the second twist he put him to his arm-pits, and the third to the base of his neck.

"Long am I seeking for you, and since you are there now you will stay there!" and he seized his sword and swept the head off him.

---

2.  tabu, obligations.

# BELGIUM

## JACQUES

Once upon a time there was a King who used to walk at night in thoughtful mood, all by himself. He looked very sad, and one night he met a man who asked him why he was so sorrowful.

"I wish I had a child," said the King. "It is the only thing I long for."

"Well, then," said the man. "You shall have a daughter; but when she is fifteen years old she must die."

Then the King was very happy. He had a daughter, and she grew to be very beautiful and very learned.

One day she read in a book that she was to die at fifteen. She went to her father and said: "Father, I must soon die."

"Keep silent, my dear daughter," he answered. "This cannot be true."

"Yes, it can," she said, "look in the book. Besides, you know it is true."

But the King did not understand a word of what was written in the book.

Then the Princess said: "Father, I have something to ask of you before I die."

"What do you want, my dear daughter?" asked the King.

"You must build me a burial vault in the church, Father," she said, "and bury me in it. And you must also put a sentry in the church so that I may find him every night at midnight."

The Princess died, and her father had a fine burial vault built, and ordered a sentry to stand in the church. At midnight the Princess blazed out of her vault like a fireball; and next day the sentry could not be found. The same thing happened on the following nights; she burnt the sentries to charcoal and then carried their bones to the rood-screen. When she had burnt nine men thus, no one else could be found who was willing to spend the night in the church; and every night she walked all round the church, saying: "Sentry, where are you?" and she also said: "Father, you don't keep your promise; Father, you don't deserve your royal crown!"

One day Jacques came to the King's house to ask for work. They said to him: "You shall have a job this evening," and that night he was sent to the church as a sentry.

Jacques felt dull all alone in the church. He wanted to take a walk, but he had been told to remain the whole night where he was. When the Princess blazed out of her vault at midnight, he was terrified and fled to the roodscreen, where he hid behind the skeletons of those who had already been burnt. The King's daughter walked all round the church, saying:

"Sentry, where are you? Father, you don't keep your promise; Father, you don't deserve your royal crown! Sentry, rescue me!"

"I would do it gladly, with God's grace," answered Jacques; but he stayed hidden where he was, and crossed himself as he spoke.

At once the Princess was released. The fire burnt out. In the morning, when the church door was opened in order to see whether Jacques had been burnt like the other sentries, he was found walking arm-in-arm with the King's daughter.

"How dare you walk with a devil's child?" cried the King; but Jacques answered:

"If your daughter is a devil's child, then you are the devil!"

And after that, Jacques and the Princess were married.


## THE OLD COBBLER

Once upon a time an old cobbler was working on the door-sill of a farm. The farmer's wife cut him a slice and bread and spread it with curds. He waited until he had finished his work before he ate it, and during that time, fifteen flies swooped down on the bread. When he saw them, he was angry. He struck the slice of bread with his fist, and there were the fifteen flies, all lying stone dead.

He went on with his work, but scarcely had he begun again when another swarm of fourteen flies swooped down on his slice of bread. Again he became very angry. He struck the bread with his fist, and there were the fourteen flies, all lying stone dead.

When he saw how true and straight was his aim, the old cobbler became vainglorious and cried out: "What a formidable blow! Fifteen and fourteen in two punches!" And he had a fine top made with the words, "I kill fifteen and fourteen of them in two punches" written upon it.

News came to the King that there was a man roving about the country and bragging that he had killed "fifteen and fourteen of them in two punches." Now the King was fighting a war at that time, and was not very sure of victory, so he summoned the old cobbler and promised him his daughter's hand in marriage if he would help him to defeat his enemies.

The cobbler dared not refuse. As he was going to join in the fight, he saw an old cross which was hanging upside down. He tried to put it back in the right position, but he could not manage to do so. So he thought he had better take it with him rather than leave it hanging in the wrong position. He loaded it on his shoulder and went on till he came to the battlefield.

When the enemies saw this man, who had killed so many people and was carrying a cross on his shoulder, they thought he must be God Himself. They knelt down at once before him to receive his blessing, which the cobbler gave them, and then he cut out off their heads, one by one.

He went back to the King and told him he had killed all the enemies.

"Just a trifle killing them!" he boasted. "I had but to show myself, and they allowed themselves to be beheaded like sheep!"

But the King did not want to give his daughter away to a cobbler, so he said:

"You cannot have my daughter unless you capture that dirty dog of a beast which is harming my country so much. It is a unicorn which ravages the woods and kills the people, and up to now nobody has been able to capture it. Go now and bring it back alive to me here."

The old cobbler went away at once. When he had been in the woods about an hour, the unicorn rushed out upon him. He just had time to take a firm stand against a stake. When the beast was on the point of driving its horn into his body, he moved quickly round the stake, and the unicorn ran its horn into the wood. The cobbler had only to pass a head-rope round its neck, and so he was able to lead it captive to the King.

"Just a trifle ensnaring this beast!" he said. "I had only to seize it by its horn to bring it to you."

And then, of course, the King was obliged to give his daughter to the old cobbler.

# FRANCE

## BLUE-BEARD

Once upon a time there was a man called Blue-Beard. He lived in Tiffauges Castle. He had already had seven wives and had killed them all. Then he married his eighth wife. One day, when preparing to go on a journey, he said to her:

"Here are all the keys of the castle. You can use them all, except this little key."

And he forbade her to enter the room to which the key belonged.

One day they had company. Blue-Beard's wife had her sister to stay with her, her sister Ann. When they passed in front of the locked room, they wanted to go in, even though it was forbidden. Inside, the seven wives were hanging! But the little key was charmed. When they opened the door, it fell into a pool of blood inside the room. Blue-Beard's wife, and her sister also, were very anxious to clean it. They boiled it, they rubbed it in ashes, but they were not able to remove the blood!

When the master returned, he asked his wife for the keys.

"Give me the keys," he said. "Will you give me this key?"

She didn't want to give it to him, but he forced her to do so. When he saw the bloodstain on the little key, he told her to go upstairs to her room, and put on her prettiest dress, to go on a journey. She went to her room, and while she was dressing, he was below sharpening his knives (for they were useless and blunt).

He shouted to his wife:

"Are you ready, wife?

> Sharpen, sharpen, my useless knives
> to cut my wife's neck!

Are you ready, wife?"

"Oh, no, no, husband. I must get my prettiest blouse.
I've never worn it, and I never will."

She had a little dog. It was on the window, and she said to it:

"Sarène, Sarène, can you see any one coming on the road to Paris?"

"Oh, no, Madam, I can see the dusty woods and the barren earth."

All this time her husband was below, sharpening his knives and calling:

"Are you ready up there, wife?

> Sharpen, sharpen, my useless knives
> to cut my wife's neck!

Are you ready up there, wife?"
  "Oh, no, no, husband. I must get my prettiest stockings.
  I've never worn them, and I never will."
  And she said to the little dog:
  "Sarène, Sarène, can you see any one coming on the road to Paris?"
  "Oh, yes, Madam, I can see a great dust-cloud coming at great speed."
  Then Blue-Beard called again:
  "Are you ready up there, wife?

> Sharpen, sharpen, my useless knives
> to cut my wife's neck!

Are you ready up there, wife?"
  "Oh, no, husband. I must get my prettiest dress.
  I've never worn it, and I never will."
  And she kept on saying:
  "Sarène, Sarène, can you see any one coming on the road to Paris?"
  "Oh, yes, Madam, I can see two horsemen far away, far away from
here."
  Then again:
  "Are you ready up there, wife?

> Sharpen, sharpen, my useless knives
> to cut my wife's neck!

Will you be ready soon, wife? I'm getting impatient!"
  "Oh, no, no, husband. I must still get my prettiest hat.
  I've never worn it, and I never will.
Sarène, Sarène, can you see any one coming on the road to Paris?"
  "Oh, yes, Madam, I can see two horsemen quite near, quite near here."
  Then again:
  "Are you ready up there, wife?

> Sharpen, sharpen, my useless knives
> to cut my wife's neck!

Will you be ready soon, wife? I'm getting impatient, I'm getting impatient."
  "I must still get my prettiest comb.
  I've never worn it, and I never will."

159

Knock, knock at the door! He was below, and he listened. Knock, knock at the door!

"Who is there?"

"Madam's brothers. We are looking for Madam."

"Madam is still getting dressed to go on a journey."

But they knew very well that this wasn't true; they had received a letter from their sister. They opened the door. On their way they had ordered a large barrel, and they had fixed some big nails all round inside it. They seized Blue-Beard and put him in the barrel, and they rolled him along the slope of La Bouillatrie among the rocks, down to the river. And the nails dug into his body! He kept calling out:

"Bouillatrie! Bouillatrie! Save my life!"

He ended in the river.

Tri-tri-tri.

My little tale is finished. I have mounted my little grey horse and I have come here.


## MARION AND JEANNE

Once upon a time there was a widower who married a widow. They both had a daughter. The widower's daughter was called Marion, and the widow's daughter was called Jeanne. The woman could not bear the sight of her husband's daughter. She was always scolding her, and telling her that she didn't work hard enough, and that Jeanne was a good worker. One day she went to the fair and bought twenty greyhounds. When she came home, she told Marion to go and look after them in the woods. When Marion went into the woods, all the greyhounds got lost. She didn't know where to find them, and she started to cry.

The Holy Virgin, who was the little girl's godmother, came to her in the woods and said:

"Why are you weeping?"

The little girl answered:

"I have reason to cry, Godmother. They bought twenty greyhounds, and they told me to watch over them, but I lost them all in the woods."

The Holy Virgin gave her a whistle, and said:

"Blow, Marion, and your greyhounds will soon come back."

Marion blew the whistle, and all the greyhounds came back. The Holy Virgin warned her to hide her whistle:

"Hide your whistle carefully in your bag, and don't tell any one about it at home."

The little girl walked on in front, her greyhounds behind her, and she led them home. Her stepmother saw her coming.

"Oh my God, here's Marion with her greyhounds."

And her daughter answered:

"Oh mother, I want to look after the greyhounds too, like Marion."

"You will lose them."

"I won't lose them, mother. Marion didn't lose them, and I won't lose them either."

Jeanne took the greyhounds into the woods. Very soon the poor little girl didn't know where to find them, and she started to cry.

"Oh, what shall I do, I have lost my greyhounds, and I cannot get them back!"

When she had cried a long while, she went back without the greyhounds.

"Here's Jeanne, but she hasn't got the greyhounds."

"Be quiet, Marion, do not scold my daughter. You go and bring back the greyhounds."

"But how can I bring them back if Jeanne has lost them in the woods?"

"Go, child," said her stepmother, "and don't talk so much. Be sure to bring them back."

When Marion reached the woods, she started to cry.

"Oh, how shall I manage to bring back the greyhounds?"

Her Godmother appeared again and said to her:

"Why are you always crying?"

"I have reason to cry, Godmother. Jeanne came to look after the greyhounds, and she lost them all, and I don't know where to find them."

"Don't cry, take your whistle from your bag and blow it."

All the greyhounds came back, and not one was missing. When Marion had gathered them all together in the woods, she walked on ahead, the greyhounds behind her, and she led them home. Jeanne saw them coming, and she cried out:

"Here's Marion with the greyhounds!"

"Be quiet, Jeanne, don't say anything," said her mother.

When Marion had tied up the greyhounds, she said:

"I had a job to get them back."

"Be quiet, Marion," answered her stepmother, "it's a good thing you had difficulty."

13

When the fire had died out, Marion's stepmother told her to go and look for some firewood.

"What shall I get it in?"

"Take your apron."

The young girl took her apron and went to look for firewood, and her apron did not catch fire. When Jeanne saw her coming back, she cried out:

"Here's Marion, and her apron has not caught fire. I want to go and look for firewood, mother."

"Don't go, Jeanne, you will set fire to your apron."

But Jeanne went to look for firewood, and her apron caught fire. Jeanne's mother told Marion to go and look for water.

"What shall I get it in?"

"Take this bucket."

Marion took the bucket, and when she reached the fountain, she put it under the tap. But the longer she held it there, the less water it contained. She did not want to go home without any water, for she was afraid her stepmother would beat her. All at once her Godmother came to her.

"Why are you always crying, Marion?" she asked.

"I have reason to cry, Godmother. They sent me to look for water with this bucket, and I cannot fill it."

"Don't cry, Marion!" And at these words, the bucket was filled with water.

"Listen, Marion, lift up your head, listen to the cock crowing."

Marion lifted up her head, and a star fell on her forehead, shining like the sun. She picked up the bucket and took it up home, full of water. Jeanne saw her coming and said to her mother:

"Here's Marion coming back with the water, with a star on her forehead that shines like the sun. Mother, I want to do the same as Marion. Give me the bucket; I want to look for water too."

"Don't go, you won't bring any back."

"Oh, mother, I want to go. Perhaps a star will fall on my forehead, and then I shall be as pretty as Marion."

Jeanne took the bucket and went in search of water, but every time she put the bucket under the fountain, it remained empty. An old woman, a sorceress, came to her and said:

"There you are, Jeanne; won't you give me a little to drink?"

"Go away," answered Jeanne, "I haven't the time, and my bucket won't fill up."

"Lift your head up in the air, Jeanne," said the old woman.

162

Jeanne lifted her head in the air, and a donkey's tail fell on her forehead. She wasn't able to fill her bucket, and she had to go home without any water. When Marion saw her coming, she said:

"Here's Jeanne coming back without any water. Oh, how ugly she is! Look at the donkey's tail on her forehead!"

"Be quiet, Marion, be quiet, Marion, leave my daughter alone; she is prettier than you."

Next day was Sunday, and Jeanne, her mother and her father went to Mass. They left Marion to look after the house, sweep it, and get the soup ready. She began to cry; she was crying when her Godmother came into the house and told her she was always crying.

"Oh, Godmother, well may I cry! They have left me to lead the cows to the pasture, to make the soup, sweep the house, and they won't let me go to Mass."

"Why won't they let you go to Mass, little Marion?"

"I have no clothes."

Her Godmother took a nut from her pocket.

"Open this nut and you will find a dress inside. Dress quickly and go to Mass, it has not yet begun. You must stay at the church door and there you will find three boys who will want to talk you, but don't stop with them. Come back quickly before Jeanne returns with her mother and father. Take your dress off and hide it in the nut."

Jeanne came back from Mass.

"Oh, little Marion, you think you're pretty, but you didn't see the girl at the church door. She was prettier than you, and she shone like the sun, and she had a prettier dress than yours."

Marion replied that she had no chance to see her because they wouldn't let her go to Mass.

"Don't worry," said Jeanne's mother to her daughter. "You are prettier than Marion. Oh, Marion, give me the scissors so that I can cut off a little hair that's hanging down here."

The following Sunday they went to Mass again, leaving Marion to look after the house. Before they went, Jeanne's mother took a basket full of feathers, and she scattered them at the top of a mountain, and told Marion to go and gather the feathers. They must all be gathered by the time she came back from Mass, without one missing. She told her also to sweep the house again and make the soup before they returned.

The wind had carried away all the feathers. Marion started to cry. Her Godmother came, and said:

"You are always crying, Marion. What's the matter?"

13·

"Well may I cry, Godmother. They left me a basket full of feathers to gather, and the wind has carried them away, and I don't know where I can find them."

"Don't cry, Marion. I will do your work for you. I will gather your feathers, I will sweep the house, I will make the soup. You go to Mass. Take this nut and crack it. Inside you'll find a pretty dress. You must wait at the church door. At the end of Mass, some boys will want to talk to you, but you must not stop with them. You must come away before the others. One of the boys will take off your shoes, but you must leave your shoes behind without turning back, and come away."

So Marion came back before the others.

"I've come back, Godmother," she said.

"Very well, take off your dress and shut it inside the nut."

"Oh, Godmother, there was a boy who took off one of my shoes. What shall I do, Godmother, without a shoe?"

"Don't grieve, little Marion. The boy will come here this evening to bring back your shoe, because he is your suitor. Now I must go, because your father and stepmother are coming back with Jeanne."

Her father, her stepmother, and Jeanne came back from Mass, and Jeanne said:

"Oh, Marion, you think you are pretty, but I saw a girl at Mass much prettier than you."

"Indeed," said Marion, "I never have the honour of going there myself, as I'm never allowed to go to Mass."

When evening came and they had eaten their supper, they saw three boys coming up from the field. Jeanne went out, and said to her mother:

"Oh, mother, here are three suitors. We must hide Marion."

"Oh, bother! Where shall we put her?"

"I know," said Jeanne, "we must hide her in the chest."

The suitors came to house and said: "Good evening!"

"Good evening, young men! Sit down."

"But we have come to see a pretty girl who lives here."

"But I am the pretty girl," Jeanne replied.

"Oh," said one of the boys, "you can't possibly be the girl I saw at the church door. That girl shone like the sun, whereas you have a donkey's tail that disfigures you."

"Something happened to my forehead, but it will soon pass."

They had a little dog, one year old, who barked every now and then. It said:

"Niaw, Niaw, you take away a donkey's tail and leave a beautiful star."

164

The boy was sitting on the chair. He got up and sat down on the chest. Inside the chest, little Marion had cracked her nut and put on her pretty dress, and now she shone like the sun. When the boy sat on the chest, she pinched him.

"Who is pinching me from inside the chest?"

"What do you think is in the chest?" said Jeanne. "There is nothing in it. Come near to me!"

But the young man got up and said: "I want to know what is inside the chest." He opened it and cried out: "Here is the young girl that I ask in marriage." And he said to her:

"You are the one whose shoe I stole at the church door."

Jeanne said: "It wasn't her, I was the one."

"Oh, well, if it was you, try on the shoe; if it fits you, you are the one."

Jeanne took the shoe, and hid in a corner with her mother. She cut her toe and her foot bled. When she had put on the shoe, she turned to the young man and said:

"It is my shoe, it fits me."

"Why have you cut your foot?" asked the young man.

"Because my foot swells in the evening."

Then Marion put on the shoe.

"This is my shoe, it doesn't belong to Jeanne."

The young man replied that he didn't want to marry Jeanne because she was too ugly; he wanted to marry Marion.

"Give me your hand, little Marion, we will get married, and we shall be happy."

"Goodbye, father, Goodbye, stepmother!"

# PORTUGAL

## THE BELL ROCK

A long time ago, there lived, not far from Citania, near Bustels, a humble shepherd and his only daughter. Only God knows how they earned their daily bread from the flocks of sheep and goats. Early in the morning, the shepherd's daughter, who was about fourteen years old, used to let her sheep go on the loveliest slopes of the mountain-chain, while her father did other work. The shepherdess was queen of all these solitary places, one moment seated in the hollows of the rocks, and next moment running after the mountain birds. At evening, warned by the sun that set in the direction of the sea, she used to return to her hut on the Bell Rock, an enormous stone that had once served as a look-out for the royal palace.

One fine morning, when she was about to shake her castagnets once again, she saw on the Bell Rock a green lizard with brightly shining eyes. Although she was very near it, and the sheep were beating the ground with their hooves, it seemed quite calm.

After that, the shepherdess scanned the rock day by day. The lizard stayed there, always quite calm, and it was perhaps because of its tranquillity that the girl gave it some milk from a white goat that had been found abandoned in Citania.

One morning, however, she saw that the beautiful white goat had no more milk, and she stood near the Bell Rock and murmured sadly: "Oh, poor little creature! I don't know what will become of you."

Next day, to her great alarm, she saw a handsome young man seated on the gravel instead of the lizard.

"Listen, little girl," he said to her. "Don't be afraid. I was changed into a lizard, and you have broken the spell. Your goodness and courage deserve a reward. For ninety days you gave me milk from this goat which you found."

The shepherdess was trembling, with her mouth wide open, and had not the strength either to shout or to escape. But the nice young man went on smiling and talking.

"Now I shall leave," he said. "Do not tell your father about this. Your happiness depends upon keeping the secret. As soon as I am safe among my relations, the white goat will get back its milk. This will be the proof that no harm has befallen me. Now listen to the end. I shall leave you this lucky charm. Guard it carefully. My journey will take three months, and at the end of that time, you must put the charm on this rock, which is the storage place for my treasures. The talisman will turn into a key, and that key will open the rock in the place that I now kiss. May Allah protect you, my angel!"

When he had said this, the young man, who seemed to have wings on his feet, walked towards the upper part of Citania, and was never seen again.

A little while afterwards, the good shepherdess became rich and beautiful. She married a wealthy farmer from Saufinius. Even when she was old, it was a pleasure to hear her tell the story of her youth.


## THE DRAWSTRING BAG

Once upon a time there was a poor washerwoman who, although old and tired, went each week to the river, taking with her the only companion she had, a niece who, when still a little girl, had lost her father and mother in a great disaster that had occurred at that time.

One day the woman fell ill. Her niece, who was very clever, looked after the house, doing everything in such a way that they always had food to eat. But this was not enough.

"May God and the Holy Virgin help me!" groaned the poor washerwoman from her bed. "If I don't get better soon, what will become of us? Who will wash all the clothes that are here?"

"I will wash them, Granny."

"You can't, my dear."

"Yes, I can, dear Granny."

"You don't know how, and besides, you are still so young."

"Yes, I know how. First, I soak the clothes, then I soap them, then I rub them, then I rinse them, then I wring them, then I hang them out and peg them. After that I dry them, and then I collect them and take them away. Next day I iron them, and I will deliver them by the end of the week. Is this the way or not, Granny?"

"Well then, go, my dear, and God be with you. But only take a little, otherwise you will be exhausted."

Little Maria, for this was the name of the washerwoman's niece, took

167

a small basket, filled it with washing, and went off to the river, light-footed. She washed and she washed and she washed all morning. Her hands ached, but when she heard midday strike in the distance, she made the sign of the cross, and all the washing she had taken with her was as white as snow in the sun.

Then she took her lunch and sat down to eat by a tree. Just then she remembered that in her hurry to get to the river and find the best place, she had forgotten to wash her face and neck. She hung her lunch-bag on a branch of a willow and took her beautiful rosary from off her neck, rolled up her sleeves, and washed herself. Then she cleaned her overall and ran back to the willow-tree.

Oh, how hungry she was, and how well she would eat in the shade of that tree!

When she had finished eating, she wanted to sleep; but no, because she had to think. She began to think about her granny and said a prayer for her. But she forgot her rosary.

The sun was still high when she reached home.

"Look, Granny, here is all the washing I've done, and so white that it smells of sunshine."

"Put it there, tomorrow is another day. Now straighten my bed, it's all upside down. Pull hard on this side. Fold the blanket on my feet, because it's too hot."

The old woman looked at her niece's neck and cried:

"Maria, what has happened to your rosary? Where have you left it?"

"Oh, Granny, I left it where I did the washing, but I will go and get it immediately before someone steals it."

And she ran out.

"Don't be late! You must still light the lamp," shouted the old woman; but her niece could no longer hear her.

In the meantime, a good-for-nothing gypsy, who was very ugly and without a trade like all gypsies, an expert at begging, one who knew all the ropes, asking here, stealing there, with his sack always on his shoulder and a stick in his hand, unshaven, and with untidy hair, happened to pass near the river. When he caught sight of the rosary, he exclaimed:

"Oh, what fine booty! Let's put it in the sack! It's worth a day's earnings."

And he put the rosary into the sack. Just then the young girl arrived, out of breath. She looked towards the washing-place and noticed the gypsy's behaviour, and she realized what had happened. With a humble voice and a pleading look, she asked:

"Have you by chance seen my necklace?"

"What necklace?"

"A rosary; it belonged to my mother."

"And where did you put this necklace?"

"I put it in the washing-place, on the top of that stone."

"Well, if you are looking for your necklace, it's here, at the bottom of my sack."

"Oh, please give it to me, dear uncle."

"Come and get it yourself."

"Get it where? I can't see it."

"Get inside the sack and there you'll see it."

As she was so small, Maria had no difficulty in getting into the sack. When the gypsy saw she was inside, he tied her up tight and went off with her. She wanted to call out, but she dared not open her mouth, because she feared the gypsy's anger and knew that he could kill her. Her mother and the Madonna would help her. And she began to pray.

The man stopped at the first door he came to.

"Give me something, lady," he said, "and I will make the drawstring bag sing."

The woman had never heard a drawstring bag sing, so she said:

"Oh, uncle, how does the drawstring bag sing?"

The gypsy put down the sack and gave the girl a pinch.

"Sing, drawstring bag, sing, sack," he said, "otherwise I will beat you with the stick."

Maria, who was afraid of being beaten, sang with a trembling voice: "I left a rosary on the stone by the river while I was washing . . ."

"Oh, how well it sings! Take this gift, and if you happen to pass by here again, knock at my door."

The gypsy went from one country to another, from door to door, and he never lacked money. One day, they told him there was an old washerwoman who had lost her niece, and because of this she was always sad and tearful. Thinking that when the washerwoman heard the drawstring bag, she would be moved and would pay him more than any one else, he went to the place where she lived. As soon as he arrived, he knocked at the door and said:

"Lady, give me something, and I will make the drawstring bag sing."

The washerwoman came to the door; she was none other than little Maria's grandmother, the gypsy's prisoner. She looked at the sack with her sad gaze, but she had no idea that the granddaughter so dear to her heart was inside.

"Whatever is this, dear uncle? I have never heard a drawstring bag sing!"

The gypsy put down the sack and, pinching it, commanded:

"Sing! Sing! Otherwise I will hit you with my stick."

Maria's voice, broken with sobs, sang more sadly than ever:

"I left a rosary on the stone by the river while I was washing . . ."

The grandmother recognised the voice of her lost granddaughter, and was just about to run to the sack; but she restrained herself in time. The gypsy was tall and strong, and the poor old woman would not have been able to do anything against such a ruffian. Moreover, looking round, she could see no one who could help her in a moment of need. Everyone was far away, working in the fields. But she had to set her little girl free. Ah, this is what she had to do.

"Look, dear uncle, the drawstring bag sings very well. Here is a small gift. It is small, I know; but as you see, I also am poor." And she added: "Here I live sadder than the night, with no desire to eat or to sleep or to work, no desire to do anything. Do you know what I would like? I would like to die. Yes, to die. I lost all my joy the day I lost her." And she began to cry.

"Who did you lose?"

"My granddaughter, who was the only joy of my old age."

"Did she die?"

"I do not know whether she is dead or alive. One day she left this house to go to the river, and she didn't come back and was never seen again. She must be wandering through the world, perhaps hungry and in rags. For this reason, there is always soup and bread in this house, and even a bed ready for those who travel from country to country to earn their living, as you do. Say that you will stay in my house tonight, and you will make me happy."

"If that is all, you can be happy. I shan't go from here. Bring me soup and milk, for I have great need of them. For a long time I haven't known what it was to eat by a fire. As for a bed, when there is one, it is only made of straw from the barn."

The girl's grandmother fed the gypsy and gave him a mug of wine to drink.

"Is this all for me?"

"All this and more, as much as you want. Drink, drink, dear uncle, and you'll see how good it is."

The man drank and drank, and only stopped when he was quite drunk. When the old woman saw he was drunk, she said:

170

"Now let's go to sleep, dear uncle."

"Yes, to sleep . . . but I'll take the sack with me, do you hear? I never leave the sack! This sack belongs to me! It's my drawstring bag. Ah, ah, ah, it's my drawstring bag, do you understand? I'll take the sack with me."

"Very well, take the sack, man of God. I don't want it; I do not lack sacks. But let us go to sleep, as it is very late."

"You're quite right. It is time to withdraw. You go on ahead with the candle, and leave me with my sack that belongs to me, do you hear?"

And the gypsy followed the old woman, holding his sack tight in his hand. When he entered the room, he got into bed without even undressing, as was his custom. In a few moments he was asleep, and snoring so loudly that you could hear him all over the house. The old woman waited no longer. Although she knew that the drunken man would not wake up before daylight, she took all necessary precautions, she walked on tiptoe, she opened the sack, and set her granddaughter free. Then she covered her with kisses, laughing and crying at the same time. But fire would have flamed from his eyes if the gypsy noticed the empty sack! So that he should not become suspicious, she put two huge cats into the sack. They were very strong and fierce.

By the first light of day, the gypsy awoke. He didn't feel very well, oh, no, for he had drunk too much the night before. But he decided to leave before the old woman remembered to ask him what he carried in the sack.

After he had walked a long way, he came to a village. The sun was high in the sky, and he had nothing to eat. So he knocked at the first door he saw, and whined in the usual way:

"Lady, give me something, and I will make the drawstring bag sing."

It was a craftsman's house, and people came from all over.

"Let's hear how the drawstring bag sings. We have never heard one sing."

The gypsy pinched the sack and commanded:

"Sing, drawstring bag, sing, sack, otherwise I will beat you with the stick."

One of the cats, feeling the pinch, cried like a condemned soul: "Miaw, Miaw!"

The gypsy gave a great kick and hit the other cat.

"Miaw, Miaw!"

The people laughed fit to burst.

"Look at the drawstring bag that miaws like a cat! Come and see the drawstring bag that cries like a cat!"

Mad with rage, the gypsy seized the cords and began to beat the sack. "Sing, drawstring bag, sing, sack!"

The more he beat the cats, the more the cats miawed: "Miaw, Miaw..."

Thinking all the time that he was talking to the drawstring bag, the gypsy beat the sack and shouted:

"You will pay me for this! Take that! And that! And that!"

But he achieved nothing, and wanting to see what had happened, he threw away the cord and untied the sack. The cats, who were furious, leapt at him and, with their claws and teeth, made his face like dough. He shouted loudly: "Oh, help me! Oh, help me!" But no one helped him, because they all realised just how bad and brutal he was.

At last, managing to free himself from the cats' mad rage, the gypsy fled, and was never seen again in that place.

## THE MERCHANT AND HIS THREE DAUGHTERS

Once upon a time there was a merchant who had three daughters. Every time he went on a journey he brought something back for each girl. One day, when he was leaving, he asked them what they would like him to bring them. The eldest asked for a ring, the middle daughter asked for a dress, and the youngest daughter for a rose.

He bought everything except the rose, which he forgot. So when he was passing a garden, he went inside and plucked a rose. And as he pulled the flower from the stem, the rose-bush uttered a very deep cry which made him tremble.

At once a giant, who was the guardian of the garden, sprang out and scolded the merchant for what he had done. He told him that, as a punishment, he would die of stomach-ache. The merchant begged for forgiveness and explained why he had plucked the rose. The giant said he could be saved from the stomach-ache if he would send him one of his daughters. So the merchant went back to his home, very sad at heart, and told the girls what had happened.

The eldest daughter hurried off to serve the giant. He gave her a very good reception. He made her mistress of the house and gave her the keys. He told her she could go all over the house, except into one room, which she must not enter until one month had passed. He also gave her a beautiful apple, and said that if she were to enter the forbidden room, the apple would fall and be bruised, and then he would know what she had done. And as a punishment for not having obeyed him, he would kill her.

The young girl could not resist the temptation. She opened the door of the room she had been forbidden to enter, and found it full of the corpses of young girls, all with their heads cut off.

The moment she opened the door, the apple fell and was badly bruised. When the giant came back and saw it, he realised that she had disobeyed him, and he cut off her head and carried her into the room where the other dead girls were. Then he sent a message to the merchant, telling him that his daughter had run away, and asking him to send another.

The middle daughter wanted to go, and she went; and the same thing happened to her as to her sister.

173

Then the youngest daughter went, but she was smarter than her sisters.

She wrapped the apple in a bundle of cloth, so that if it fell on the ground it would not be bruised. The days passed by, and the giant was very surprised to find that this girl was not curious like the others.

One day he asked her to clean his hair. She made him lay his head in her lap, and she combed his hair until he fell asleep. Then she cut off his head with a penknife. The beheaded giant spoke with difficulty and told her where to find a jar of ointment with which she could fix his head on again.

She found the ointment and put his head on again; but she put it on back to front. The giant, in desperation, jumbed about like a devil, and beat his head against the walls, and cried, "Bab – bab". He could not say anything else, and did not know what he was doing, and as a result of knocking his head so often, he died.

The young girl took the ointment and mended her sisters' heads and those of all the other girls, and they all came back to life. Then the sisters ran back home. They found their father much aged, but when he saw them he was filled with joy.

## THE DRAGON

Near a beautiful city where a King lived, there was a large cavern, and in this cavern an enormous serpent, called Dragon, was hiding. This big serpent ate many people. The inhabitants of the city made a pact with him, that each year they would give him a girl, provided that he left all the other people in peace. All the heads of families drew lots to see which of the girls would have to be given to the dragon, and the lot fell on the King's daughter.

So the King made it known throughout his kingdom that whosoever would free his daughter from the dragon could marry her and be heir to the throne.

When the appointed day arrived, the King's daughter was tied to a tree.

Many people, full of curiosity, climbed up the neighbouring trees. There was no one to be seen on the earth. However, shortly before the dragon appeared, a shepherd came to that place, leading a dog at his side. He said to the girl who was bound to the tree: "What are you doing here?" and when he heard from her what was happening, he sat down behind the tree, holding his dog near to him.

Suddenly, the dragon appeared with a roar. Then the shepherd said to his dog:

"Caesar, fetch him."

The dog caught hold of the gigantic animal and tore it to pieces. Then the shepherd unbound the girl.

The King's servants, who were in the neighbouring trees, came down, and dressed their young mistress in seven skirts. One man cut off the dragon's seven heads and put them in a large sack, which he took home with him. But before the heads were put into the sack, the shepherd cut the tongues from each of the seven heads, and he also cut a little piece from each of the seven skirts that the King's daughter had put on.

The King held a great banquet, "the bachelor's farewell". In the place of honour sat the King, his daughter, and her fiancé, who was the man who had put the seven heads in the sack. No one – not one of the King's courtiers – had invited the shepherd to the feast. Towards the end, and without any one noticing, he appeared, accompanied by his dog. Three times he sent Caesar in search of a plate of food. The King's daughter grew angry when she saw the dog, because she recognised him, and the King ordered his men to tie up the dog, which meanwhile had gone back to his master, the shepherd.

Then the shepherd stood up and presented himself to the King. He said:

"This dog of mine killed the dragon; and consequently, I am the man who should marry the King's daughter, according to your promise."

Then there was great confusion. The fiancé, who was sitting at the table, presented the dragon's seven heads upon a great tray, saying:

"I killed it."

"There is something missing from these heads," replied the shepherd. "I have here the seven tongues from the heads, which I kept in the pieces of the seven skirts belonging to the young girl."

So he became the girl's husband, and son-in-law and heir to the King.

# ITALY

## THE BLACK BRIDE AND THE WHITE BRIDE

Once upon a time there was a poor man whose wife had died. He had an only child called Graziosa who was like a ray of sunshine; but later, he married again, and his second wife also had a daughter called Bertuccia, as ugly as sin, and as can be imagined, the stepmother loved her own daughter more than Graziosa, and she treated Graziosa worse than a servant.

One day the stepmother, who didn't know how to make her stepdaughter grow ugly, thought of sending her to the fairies, on the pretext of getting the sieve. Poor Graziosa walked on and on, along the road that led to the place where her stepmother had told her to go. At a certain point on the road she met an old woman, who asked her where she was going.

"I am going to the fairies to get the sieve," she said.

"Listen carefully to what I tell you," said the old woman. "When you reach the door where the fairies live, knock quietly, and you'll see a kitten come to open the door. It will ask you what you are looking for. You must answer that you want to see the fairies. Be careful – the stairs are made of glass, go up them with care, for if you break one of the steps, it will be your downfall. When you reach the top, you'll see an unmade bed. You must make it. Be careful – there will be some dirty insects. Don't take any notice, and when the fairies ask you what you've found there, you must say, 'Diamonds and rubies.' Then they will ask you to comb their hair. You must say 'Yes,' and you'll find insects, but when they ask you what you've found, you must reply, 'Pearls and sapphires.' Now go on your way."

As soon as she arrived, the young girl did what the old woman had told her. A kitten really did come to open the door, and asked her:

"What are you looking for?"

"I want to see the fairies," answered Graziosa.

Then she went up the stairs carefully, and when she was at the top she saw the bed was not made, so she made it with care. The fairies asked her:

176

"What did you find?"

"Diamonds and rubies," she answered.

"Diamonds and rubies you shall have," they said. "Listen, will you do us a favour and comb our hair?"

"Willingly," she answered.

When she had combed their hair carefully, they asked the same question, and she answered:

"Pearls and sapphires."

"Pearls and sapphires you shall have," said they. "Now what do you want?"

"Mother sent me to get the sieve," she answered.

"First come with us," said the fairies, and they led her to a room full of precious stones, and said to her:

"Choose at will."

The young girl took the smallest that was there, and the fairies took it away and gave her the loveliest stones; then they took her to a room full of dresses and they bade her choose one. She took the most modest, the one that cost least. The fairies changed it for a beautiful dress made of gold and precious stones. Graziosa thanked them, took the sieve, and went away. But the fairies called her back and said to her:

"When you reach the bridge, you'll hear the donkey bray. Do not turn round. Then you'll hear the cock crow – turn round."

When the young girl was on the bridge, she heard the donkey bray indeed, but she didn't turn round. Then she heard the cock crow, and she turned round. As soon as she had done so, a beautiful star fell on her forehead, shining so brightly that it was impossible to look at it. When she arrived home she knocked at the door. The stepmother came to open it, and when she saw such splendour, she was very angry because the girl was even lovelier than before. She thought of sending Bertuccia to take back the sieve.

Bertuccia went, and on the way, instead of the old woman, she met a young girl who asked her:

"Where are you going?"

"I'm going where I please," answered Bertuccia.

The young woman was indignant at such an answer and said to her:

"Go where you like, and it will serve you right!"

The girl knocked at the door hard enough to knock it down. The same kitten came to open it, and he asked the same question.

She replied: "I'm looking for what I please. What has it to do with you?"

14

Then she went up the glass stairs roughly and broke three or four steps. When she was at the top, the fairies said to her:

"Will you make our bed?"

She answered: "I've come here to take the sieve, not to be your servant."

She made the bed any old how, and the fairies asked her:

"What have you found in the bed?"

"Filth!" she replied.

"And filth you shall have," they answered. "Listen, will you comb our hair?"

"Oh, what a bore!" she said; but she combed their hair, and the fairies asked her:

"What did you find?"

"Revolting insects," she said.

"And insects you shall have," they answered. Then, as they had done with her sister, they took her to the room full of precious stones. Bertuccia chose the loveliest ones, but the fairies took them away from her and gave her the ugliest. Then they led her to the room full of dresses, and she took one, a marvellous one, but the fairies did as before. She started to leave, but they called her back, and said to her:

"Be careful, when you go over the bridge, you'll hear the donkey bray. Do not turn round; but when you hear the cock crow, then turn round."

When she was on the bridge that the fairies had mentioned, she did exactly the opposite, because she was angry at what they had done; but it was so much the worse for her, for she grew a donkey's tail that hung down to the ground. Then she began to sing out: "Mamma, look, look, the donkey's tail is hanging down." When her mother saw her daughter coming in such a state, she burst out crying.

A few days after that, the King's son fell in love with Graziosa and married her. They held a feast and a banquet, and they didn't give me a bite to eat.


## THE THREE ORANGES

Once upon a time there was a peasant who went to look for godparents for his daughter's christening. But he got lost on the way. He went this way and that, and finally he ended in a wood, dying with hunger and thirst. He threw himself down on a tree trunk and began to cry.

He had hardly sat down when he saw a very ugly woman passing by with a basket on her back. She said to him:

"You're very thirsty, I know, but if you want refreshment, go to the palace at the top of that wooded hill. When they see you coming, they will open the door immediately. But I advise you, for your own sake, to do as I tell you.

First of all, you must grease the door with soap; then sweep the stairs well. When you've done that, go into the kitchen. There you'll find a lot of cats working busily, some washing the dishes, some drying them, and others sweeping the floor. You must go straight on till you come to a room where you'll find a lot of dogs, some beating the carpet, others dusting, others cleaning the windows, and two sweeping the floor. You must carry straight on and go into another room. Here you'll find a group of people, and on the walls you'll see a lot of hooks like those butchers use, and hanging on the hooks you'll see the bodies of people who a short time ago were still alive. Carry straight on, and go into the last room. There you'll find a woman sitting on a divan and stroking a donkey's head on her knees. When she sees you, she will ask you a lot of questions, so as to find out what you've seen before reaching her. On the cupboard you'll see three beautiful oranges; take them and put them in your pocket, they will be your fortune. The woman will start asking you how you found the castle. Tell her that you've never had the chance to see such a beautiful thing before; then say: 'First I saw a beautiful porch as bright as if it had been made yesterday, stairs so clean that you could throw polenta made from white flour on them; fine servants and cooks in the kitchen; in one room, splendid servants busy at their work; in another room, a lot of pork hanging on hooks that would make you want to eat it raw; then here I saw you, madam, kissing a handsome young man.'"

The peasant did all that the woman had told him to do. The lady seated on the divan said to him:

"You have set me free with your answers. I have been here for more than a century, as a penance. Take these oranges on the cupboard, and you'll be happy for the rest of your life."

When she had finished speaking, she struck the earth with a wand. The palace started to tremble as if there were an earthquake, and soon afterwards it fell into ruins. The peasant found himself again in the middle of the wood, as if by a miracle, but this time he was near a fountain, and so he was able to quench his thirst without having resort to the oranges.

He walked on and on. He met a man and a woman, who asked him where he was going in such despair.

"My wife has a daughter," he said, "and I have no godparents for the christening."

14ᐧ

"We'll act as godparents," said one of them. "I am Death, and this is the Wind."

"I," said Death, "will teach you a profession that will make you rich. You have only to spread the rumour that you are a doctor. When people call you to visit a sick person, and you see me at the foot of the bed, that person will certainly get better. Then, to play the part, you must give him a brew of herbs. Don't be afraid, however, if something happens to you as well, because the four laws of man are: first, spectacles, second, the stick, third, the hump, and fourth, the balloon."

The Wind then promised, as a gift, to blow no longer on his fields, and in fact, everything happened as the godparents had said.

He set up as a doctor, and people came from all over to be examined by him, and with the years he became very rich. The Wind's gift was not so good, because the plants in his fields became full of spiders' webs as big as sheets. In fact, he went back to the woods to talk to the Wind, but he could not find him. Meanwhile, the years passed by. One day he fell ill. When his wife saw Death at the head of the bed, he didn't want to die, and he told her to turn the bed round, so as to have Death at the foot of the bed. But this was of no avail, and he, too, had to go back to his Creator.

In his will he advised his daughter to go and peel the oranges in the wood where he had met her godparents. As she wanted to respect and obey her father's wishes, the girl went into the woods. As she walked along the road, she became very thirsty. She peeled an orange, but when she began to open the slices, a girl jumped out and said to her:

"Give me a little water to drink, I beg you, otherwise I shall die of thirst."

But the doctor's daughter was unable to help her, and the poor girl died on the spot. She continued on her way, and peeled another orange to quench her thirst. Another girl jumped out, and died immediately afterwards because she could find nothing to drink.

At last, when she had walked a long way, the doctor's daughter found a fountain where she could quench her thirst. Near it, she peeled an orange, and a beautiful girl jumped out; she also refreshed herself at the fountain, but as soon as she had stopped drinking, she disappeared as if by enchantment, and the doctor's daughter suddenly found herself as naked as God had made her. After a while, she saw a woman who was a witch, and who said to her:

"What are you doing, poor child?"

180

The girl answered that she was waiting for her fiancé, who was the King's son.

"Very well," said the witch. "Wait till I comb your hair because it is all dishevelled."

The girl let her comb her hair, but the witch put three pins into it, and these pins turned the girl into a dove that at once flew away.

The witch undressed, and waited for the King's son, pretending to be the doctor's daughter. At last he arrived, with all his servants, in a coach drawn by six horses. Inside the carriage were dresses for the bride, made of silk, such as Queens wear. When the King's son saw the witch, he said:

"How ugly you have become!"

"What can you expect?" she answered. "What with the rain and the sun, terrified by fierce beasts, I have become like this; but after I've been with you for eight days, I shall be as before."

The witch dressed with great splendour, and when she climbed into the coach, the horses started to run like the wind.

Next day, there was a great reception at the King's palace, with a hundred guests in honour of the bride. The cooks were busy working round the big stove in the kitchen, cooking the finest dishes, when they saw a little dove land on the window and start to sing:

"Cook, cook, fine cook, fall asleep!
Roast, roast, burn so that the witch can't eat!"

A long time passed, and the guests began to get impatient for the food. They sent servants to the kitchen to see what had happened. They found the kitchen full of smoke, the meat all burnt, the saucepans burst, and the cooks asleep on the floor as though drunk, snoring like bassoons. The King's son ordered the cooks to be woken up, and he had them brought before him, to find out the reason for such great shortcomings. The cooks told him of the little dove that had come to sing at the kitchen window and had made them fall asleep. Then the King gave orders for the bird to be caught, if it were to reappear.

In fact, when the cooks started cooking again, the little dove reappeared. They caught it, and took it to the big dining-room where the guests and the bride and bridegroom were assembled.

As soon as the witch saw the dove, she started to scream like a mad woman:

"Throw it away, it's a wicked witch, and I don't want to see it near me!"

181

But the guests began to stroke it, and one, while stroking its head, drew out the three pins. Then the dove immediately turned into the doctor's daughter, who found herself, naked against her will, in front of her fiancé and all the guests. The servants ran to look for clothes for her, and in a short time they came back with a dress made of gold brocade, and embroidered with flowers that shone like the sun and moon together. The girl told them all that the witch had done to take her fiancé away from her.

Then the King's son ordered his servants to seize the witch and drag her into the courtyard and tie her to four horses – two at her feet and two at her arms; and to beat her soundly, and then to have her quartered.

When the bride and the bridegroom and the guests saw this unexpected sight, they laughed and clapped for joy that the witch had not been able to carry out her evil plan.

## THE SERPENT SON

Once upon a time there was a King and a Queen, and they had no son. The Queen made vows and did penance; but she never had any children. She went round the countryside and saw all the animals, and she said:

"All the animals have children. The little glow-worms have them; the little snakes have them; the little birds have them; I alone have none!"

She saw a serpent, and she said: "I'd even be glad of a serpent!" So she conceived, and everyone was happy. Nine months later, there was a great banquet; they were all ready for the Queen to deliver a child, but this Queen had a serpent. Everyone was amazed, but the mother was quite satisfied. A beautiful iron cage was made and the serpent was put into it. The maid prepared his food, the same as they all ate, in the morning, soup and the other dishes likewise, and so at midday and in the evening.

The serpent ate enough for two and grew every day. When he was quite big, the maid went to make his bed, and she heard a voice saying:

"Tell Papa that I want a little wife here, rich and beautiful!"

The girl was frightened, but the Queen made her enter the cage. The serpent said the same thing as before. Once again the maid told the Queen, and the Queen said: "What must we do?"

She had a dependent, a peasant, and she said to him:

182

"I will give you as much as you want if you will give me your daughter."

She gave the daughter to the serpent, and they were married. They ate together, and at night the serpent turned into a man. When morning came, he said to her:

"What's the time?"

"My father gets up at this time," said the bride, "and goes out to dig; it's four o'clock."

"Oh, you're a peasant's daughter!" he cried, and he drew out his sword and cut her throat. The maid came in, bringing his soup, and she saw the dead girl. The serpent said he wanted to marry again, and he wanted a bride who was rich and beautiful. And so it went on for several days. At last, the Queen gave him the dead girl's sister. They were married, but three days afterwards, he killed her as well after he had asked her the time.

When the maid took him his food and saw that the other girl was dead too, she was even more afraid than before. He said the same thing to her:

"Tell Papa that I want a little wife here soon, rich and beautiful!"

The maid told the Queen, and she said:

"What shall we do? He has killed two wives. Who will give his daughter to my son?"

The serpent made a great noise, saying he wanted a suitable wife. The peasant had no more daughters, for he had only had two. However, there was a cobbler who lived opposite, who was very poor, and had an only daughter, who was beautiful. They asked him for her, and when he heard they were going to give him money, he said "Yes" at once. He received a lot of money, and in return he gave his daughter to the serpent. One Saturday night, a couple of days after the wedding, the serpent asked his wife what time it was. She turned round and said:

"At this time my father works at his bench."

When the serpent, who was a man at that moment, heard this, he drew out his sword and cut off her head.

Next morning, the maid came and saw what had happened, and she told the Queen that her son had killed this wife as well, and now he wanted another, beautiful and wealthy. He kept on complaining and shouting that he wanted a good wife, and so the King wrote to an Emperor who had been his best man. The Emperor had one daughter and no others. He agreed at once to the King's request, but they made a pact. The Princess took a month to decide. She took a louse and put it in a box, and cared for it each day. The louse grew big during the month, and its skin was like that of a sheep. They took off this skin and put it in a box. The bride's mother took it to the serpent and said, from outside the cage, that if he could guess what skin it was, they would give him their daughter.

The serpent was bewitched, and pretended to think it was a flea's skin or a sheep's skin. He named many animals and each time the bride's mother said "No". Then she said:

"Well then, don't you want my daughter?"

When he heard this, he said: "It's a louse's skin." He had guessed. So they gave him the girl.

That evening they were married. All were invited. They had concerts, balls and entertainments, and played music until dawn. Each morning the couple went to bed, and dances were held for three days.

Three days after the wedding, the Empress went back to her own city. The serpent said to his wife:

"If you want me to be a man by day as well as by night, you have but one thing to do."

"I will do what you want, husband. What do you want me to do?"

"My mother gives many balls and concerts. You will see that they will tell you to dance at these, but you must not dance with any one. When you see me coming in at the door, dressed in red, then you must get up from your chair and dance."

That evening they had company and began to dance. They knew that the serpent was in his cage, but they didn't know that he became a man at night. They asked the Princess to dance, but she refused, and said she preferred to sit. This seemed a dreadful thing to the King and Queen, that she should cut such a bad figure.

Suddenly the Princess saw her husband coming in, dressed in red, and she began to dance with him. When the dance was over, the King and Queen took her by the hair and dragged her all through the house.

"Is this the way you behave with us?" they said. "Be careful not to do the same thing tonight!"

She went to bed aching and sad. She told the serpent, and he said:

"Well, don't take any notice, for you still have two days to suffer. This evening when they invite you, don't dance. If they hit you, they hit you; it doesn't matter! But when you see me dressed in black, come out and dance."

That evening the Princess refused to dance with the King or the Princes, or with any one. She only danced with the man dressed in black, and

184

when he had gone, she sat down again. When everyone had left, her relatives said to her:

"Every evening you make a scene, and make us suffer so!"

They picked up an iron bar and began to hit her. They hit her without pity! The poor girl could not bear it any longer and, aching all over, she went and told her husband. He said to her:

"Well, wife, don't worry. You have only one more evening to suffer. Tomorrow evening, when I come dressed as a friar, dance with me; but do not dance with the others."

That night they all invited her to dance, but she would not. Her husband came, dressed as a friar, and they danced together. All at once, when the King and Queen saw her dancing with that man, they took a stick and, in front of all the guests, started beating in every direction.

Suddenly the friar turned into a large and ugly bird. It broke the window in its flight, and away it went. The King and Quen were so shocked that they began beating the bride almost to death. When they discovered that the friar was their son, they nearly died of grief. They loved that girl; but what was done was done.

One morning, the Princess took two bags of money and went away. She met a man with glassware, who was weeping. She asked him what was the matter.

"A furious bird passed by and broke all my glassware."

"How much was it worth?"

"My master said it was worth fifty lire."

She opened her bag and paid him. Then she asked:

"Which way did it go?"

"This way – straight ahead."

She walked on and on, and came to a jeweller's shop. The owner was absent, but a boy was there, weeping. The Princess asked him what was the matter.

"A furious bird flew by and did all this damage. Now my master is coming and he'll kill me."

"How much is all this gold worth?"

"Leave me alone! I have great sorrow."

"No," she said. "I want to pay you because it was my bird."

He estimated everything and added it up to an exaggerated sum. He calculated the damages at six thousand lire. Besides other damages, he reckoned three thousand five hundred for himself and five hundred for the owner.

"Which way did it go?" asked the Princess.

"Straight ahead."

She went on her way. When the shop assistant saw such a great sum of money, he paid his master, left the shop, and opened a shop of his own which sold everything – bread, pasta, and flour.

The Princess walked on and on. Suddenly she saw a huge bird, and she cried: "O, I think perhaps it's my bird!" She climbed up a tree and, sad at heart, she begged the bird to come home with her. All the other birds understood why, and they begged it to go, but it would not. Because she was obstinate, it pecked out her eye. But even with one eye missing, she still begged it to go with her. Then it pecked out her other eye. The unhappy girl was now blind and could not see where she was going. She begged it to accompany her, but it stubbornly refused. It pecked her again and cut off her arm. She said:

"Poor me! What shall I make of my life? I am blind and maimed."

She started off, and presently she met an old woman, who was really the Madonna.

"What's the matter, pretty one?" she asked.

The Princess told her what had happened. While she was telling her the story, the bird flew above its mother's roof and turned into a man. His mother, for joy and delight, invited everyone. She made him tell her everything, and she said:

"You did well to kill that ugly woman!"

Meanwhile, his bride was talking to the Madonna, who said to her:

"Put your arms into this fountain until the blood flows out."

She washed herself and saw her hands appear. The water in the fountain was all red with blood. When she had washed, she dried herself with her dress.

"Now wash your face," said the Madonna.

She washed her face, and her eyes came back, and she was more beautiful than before. Then the Madonna said to her:

"Walk straight ahead!"

She had hardly gone two steps when the Madonna turned round and gave her a wand, saying: "Ask this wand, and you will get whatever you wish for."

She asked for a fine palace in front of the King's, and suddenly a beautiful palace sprang up, made of diamonds inside and out. Within there was a broody hen with gold chicks. There were many gold birds that could walk; there were servants and gatekeepers. The Princess sat in an armchair, covered with veils.

In the morning, the King's son opened the window and looked out, as was his custom, and he saw the palace.

"Oh, Father!" he cried. "How beautiful!"

They looked inside, but they couldn't see anything but golden animals that could walk. The Prince said to his father:

"How rich they must be to have built this palace overnight!"

As he spoke, his eyes fell on the Princess, and she lifted her veils from her face. The King's son said in amazement:

"Oh, Papa! How beautiful she is! I want her for my bride."

"Get away with you! Whatever are you saying? Who knows who she is? And if she'd want you! Don't ask her, for she doesn't want you."

The King's son insisted, and he sent her a handkerchief embroidered in gold. His wife threw it to the chicks and the broody hen, and took no notice of him. The maid told the Prince, and his mother and father said to him:

"We told you. She doesn't want you."

"Well, I want her," he said; and he asked for her hand again. He sent her a ring, and she threw it to a bird. Then the maid said she wouldn't go into that house again. He told her to go again, but she didn't want to go. Then what did the Prince command? He ordered a coffin, and told them to put him inside it, without the lid, and to carry him under the Princess' window. As they passed by, she looked out; and in a second, the Prince climbed on to the balcony and began to talk to her.

His wife told him quite plainly that she didn't want him, and she said:

"Do you remember what you did to me?"

The Prince, who was no longer bewitched, didn't recognise her. She said to him:

"You did this and that. Your father beat me and your mother mal-treated me. The first, second and third evening when you said I must dance with you, and that it was the last evening ... was it not true, then?"

He answered: "If you hadn't danced with me as I told you, then I would still be a serpent."

She turned round and said:

"And when you were a bird, were you also a serpent? And when you cut off my arm and blinded me, and then had me killed and cut into pieces? But fortunately I found someone who healed me."

The Prince was amazed, and he said:

"And if I hadn't blinded you and cut off your arm, how could I have become a man? I should have remained a bird."

"You are right," said the Princess. "Since this is so, let us get married and be husband and wife, as is only right."

The Prince was delighted, and he went straight to his parents and told them all about it. Then they both went to visit the Princess, and they talked together.

"I couldn't dance with you or the others," said the bride, "because he told me not to do so, when he was a serpent, otherwise he would not have become a man."

"And couldn't you have told me?"

"No, otherwise he would have remained a serpent. And how far I walked and how much I suffered to find him again! And then, at last, I found him, and he was brutal enough to blind and maim me! How much pain I suffered, only I know. If it had been any other woman, she would not have cared about him."

When his mother heard all this, she made excuses, saying:

"I didn't know, and so you must forgive me."

So they made it up, and the Empress was written to about it. She came with the Emperor, and they were all happy. The young couple were married in the palace made of diamonds, and for a month there were balls and concerts. Then the two came back to their city, and lived happy and contented after so much suffering.

> The tale is told
> and let's throw away the hat.

# GREECE

## THE VILE MOTHER-IN-LAW

There were once three girls who had lost their parents. The eldest spun wool, the second carded it, and the third worked it.

The King, at one time, decreed that there should be no lights at night. Who most lamented this decree? The three sisters. One said to the others:

"What shall we do, who till now have worked at night as if it were day?"

The youngest sister said:

"Will you hear the notion I have had? Let us go and clean out the rain-water-tank; then let us take three chairs, and work on our wool at night there, that we may not waste time."

A neighbour discovered them and told the King's watchman that there was a light at night in the water-tank, and that three girls sat working there. The King's watchman went and made them pay a fine in gold.

The maidens spoke. The first and eldest said:

"If I had the King for my husband, I would bear him the Sun and the Moon."

The second said:

"If I had the King's cook for my husband, I would bake him such a cake as could be shared by all his army."

The youngest said:

"If I had the King's coachman for my husband, I would work him a belt that would flash round his waist like lightning."

The maidens laughed together. The King's watchman left them and went back to the King.

"My lord King! In all the country I found but one light in a tank. I demanded a fine, and spoke to three maidens. The first said, 'If I had the King for my husband, I would bear him the Sun and the Moon.' The second said, 'If I had his cook for my husband, I would make him such a cake as would feed all his army.' And the third said, 'Had I his coachman for my husband, I would work him a belt that would flash like lightning round his waist'."

Said the King to him: "Go and fetch these maidens here."

The watchman went and said to them:

"Good day, maidens! The King bids you come to him."

"What does the King want with us?" asked the girls.

"Fear not," he said, "Come."

So the maidens went before the King. No sooner had they come before him than he said to them:

"I wish you to tell me the tales you were telling last night."

"We told no tales, lord King," they replied.

"Tell me!" he commanded.

"We were jesting, lord King. I said that had I the King for my husband, I would bear him the Sun and the Moon."

"And what did you say?" he asked the second sister.

"I said that if I had his cook for a husband, I would make him such a cake as would feed his army."

"And you, the youngest, what was it you said?"

"I said that had I his coachman for my husband, I would work him a belt that would flash like lightning about his waist."

"Your wishes are granted," said the King. And he married the second sister to his cook, the youngest to his coachman, and he himself married the eldest who had said she would bear him the Sun and the Moon.

The second and youngest sister were as good as their word, and did what they said they would do. The King set up house with the eldest sister. After a while, the Queen knew herself to be with child.

The King was commanded to go to the wars. Before he departed from the palace, he said to his mother:

"As soon as the Queen is delivered of her child, you must send me word whether it be the Sun or the Moon."

The mother replied:

"It shall be as you wish, my son."

The Queen's mother-in-law hated the Queen because she was of humble birth. When the time of childbirth drew near, the mother-in-law said to the Queen:

"I will go and bring the midwife, that she may tend you."

When the midwife came, the mother-in-law said to her:

"I will give you a hundred pounds if, when the Queen's child is born, be it Sun or Moon, you take good care to slay it."

"Rest assured," said the midwife, and she took her leave of the mother-in-law.

Fourteen days and nights passed. The Queen was in labour, and the midwife came to her. When the child was born, the whole place was lit by a bright light, for she had given birth to the Sun. The midwife at once wrapped the baby in a cloth and gave it to the mother-in-law in such a way that the woman in childbed did not see her do it.

The mother-in-law took out of her bag a young dog wrapped in a cloth, and placed it beside her son's wife, saying:

"Grieve not that you have given birth to a dog. It is God's will."

The Queen was very unhappy that she had not been able to carry out her promise, as her sisters had done.

The midwife shut the child inside a chest, and took it to the seashore, where grew a bed of rushes. There she hid it. An old man was fishing a little way from the shore. He saw the woman place a chest in the bed of rushes and go away. He went then and picked up the chest and took it home with him.

When the chest was opened, the house was lit by a bright light. The fisherman said to his aged wife:

"You must raise the child, and you must let no stranger into the house. I will go to the bay and fish."

The King came joyfully home from the wars. He asked his mother for news, and she told him that his wife had given birth to a dog. When he heard this, his heart almost broke with sorrow; but his mother said to him: "Patience, my son."

In a little while, the Queen was once again with child. At the end of nine months, the King was again commanded to go to the wars. He left his wife in his mother's hands, saying:

"Mark well! We shall see what sort of child she will bear."

Seven days and nights passed, and then the Queen felt the pangs of childbirth. The midwife was called, and the mother-in-law said to her:

"I will give you another hundred pounds if my daughter-in-law should give birth to a child the like of the other, and you slay it."

In a little while, the Queen gave birth to the Moon, and as she was delivered of the child, the house was lit by a bright light.

Hastily the midwife wrapped the baby in a cloth and gave it to the mother-in-law, who placed a kitten by the Queen's side. The kitten mewed. When the woman in childbed saw it, she swooned. The mother-in-law and the midwife revived and comforted her.

"Grieve not so sorely," said the mother-in-law, "you will have another child."

The midwife took the child, put it in a chest, and carried it down to the bed of rushes. The old man was once again fishing in the bay. When the woman had set down the chest and gone, he drew near and took it home.

"Wife! What was it I told you? Now we have the Moon as well as the Sun."

The King returned from war. What should he see but his mother bowed down with grief? She told him that, instead of the Moon, his wife had given birth to a kitten.

The King could no longer bear the sight of his wife. He called two of his henchmen and bade them open up the sewer, put the Queen within, and seal it up anew. The dog and the cat which she was supposed to have borne were drowned.

The old man and his wife cared for the Sun and the Moon. After a time, the old woman died, and the old man fell ill. The children were then seven years of age.

The old man said to the Sun: "O Sun, my child, good fortune betide you. I am dying. I leave you the pony so that, whatever the Moon should ask of you, you may go and bring it to her."

Then he died, and the brother and sister were left alone. One day, when they were sitting together on their balcony, they saw the King pass by below with two of his henchmen. When the King saw them on the balcony, he halted and said to himself:

"If my wretched wife had had such children as these, how proud and happy I should be now!"

Then he went up to the children. He besought them to give him a cup of water, and asked: "Where are your father and mother?"

"They are dead," they replied. "We are alone."

"Will you not come to the palace on Sunday," asked the King, "to eat with me?"

"We thank you, O King. We will come."

The King told his mother about the Sun and the Moon, and he said to her: "If they were mine, how happy I should be!"

"Where do they dwell?" she asked; and he answered: "On such-and-such a road."

The King's mother went to seek out the children. The Moon was alone. The King's mother said to her:

"Sweet child, and how do you do? Where is your brother?"

"He has taken our horse to pasture," said the Moon.

"Does your brother love you?" asked the King's mother.

"That he does. Whatever I ask of him, he will do."

The King's mother answered: "Tell him to bring you the water of life, and you will see if he loves you."

192

Then she left her. In a little while the Sun returned, and found the Moon pretending to be sick.

"What ails you, my sister?" asked the Sun.

"I want you to go and bring me the water of life to make me well."

"Then I will go," he said.

As he went on his way, he heard a voice saying: "Two go forth, none shall return."

He saw a small house before him. He went to the door and found a young woman there. He said to her:

"Good day to you, foster-mother."

"God give you a good day, Sun. What is it you seek?"

"My sister is sick and demands the water of life."

She said to him: "This water of life that you seek is in a mountain which opens and shuts, and you cannot easily take the water from it. But I will give you a counsel. Take this flask. Go to the top of the mountain and as soon as it opens, gallop inside on your horse, quickly fill the flask and, when the mountain opens again, hasten out with all speed and bring me the water you have taken."

The Sun went, fetched the water as the woman had told him, and gave it to her. She poured it over the mountain, and all those who had been lost therein were brought back to life, and the mountain opened, never to close again.

The Five-times-fair One put some drinking water in the flask for him, and he took it to the Moon. She sprinkled some on her head and became well again.

Next day, the King's mother went to see the Moon again, and asked her whether her brother had brought her the water of life.

"That he did," answered the Moon.

"Now tell him to fetch you the water-melon of life," said the King's mother.

When the Sun returned, the Moon pretended to be sick and besought him to fetch her the water-melon of life. He set out, and went to the Five-times-fair One's house, and told her what the Moon had asked him to do.

"You must fetch this water-melon," she said to him, "from the place where it is guarded by forty dragons, and you hear it speak. Give heed to what I say! Go into the hut, and you will see the water-melon within, surrounded by forty dragons. Get underneath it and hide there. Make as if to cut it, and it will speak and say, 'I am cut!' But you must lie hidden.

15

When you touch it again, and it does not speak, then cut it and bring it to me."

The Sun took hold of the water-melon, and it cried out: 'I am cut!' The dragons rose up and looked about them, but they saw no one. He took hold of it again, and the water-melon cried out yet again. The dragons looked about them and saw no one. They said to her:

"Cry out no more, or we will cut you into forty pieces."

Yet again the Sun took hold of it. This time the water-melon did not speak. He cut it and took it to the Five-times-fair One. She took it and gave him another in its stead, and this one he took to the Moon.

Next day, the King's mother went to see the Moon, and asked her:

"Did the Sun bring you the water-melon?"

"That he did."

"Now tell him to bring you forty dragons to guard the house, lest you should be carried off."

When the Sun came in, the Moon said to him:

"I am afraid. Go and bring me forty dragons to guard the house, lest I be carried off."

He said to her, "I will go and bring them for you," and he went to the Five-times-fair One.

"How will you manage all the forty dragons?" she said to him. "Take this hair. When you are three yards outside your house, put a light to it, and the forty dragons will appear, and say: 'What is your will, master?' Then take them and set them to guard your house."

He brought home the dragons.

On Saturday morning, the King's mother again went to see the Moon. No sooner had she crossed the threshold than the dragons rushed to devour her. But the Moon had seen her, and said to them:

"Touch her not, she is my grandam."

The King's mother went in, and she said:

"Now I have seen that your brother loves you truly, and that is well for him. Tomorrow we shall expect you to come to our house and eat with us."

The Sun mounted his horse and went to the Five-times-fair One. He told her that the King had invited them to the palace. But she said:

"Go you shall not, unless I go with you."

On Sunday morning the Five-times-fair One made ready a bag. Inside it she put a kitten and a young dog. Then she called for the children, and they all set off for the palace, where they were received.

When the table was laid for the meal, the King's mother put poison in the children's plates. Bidding them come to the table and eat, she showed them the plates and said:

"This is the Sun's plate, and this is the Moon's."

The Five-times-fair One said to the children: "Do not begin to eat unless I bid you."

The King and his mother paid great heed to the Five-times-fair One. She said to the King: "Take not amiss what I do here, O King."

She opened her bag, took out the young dog and the kitten, and put the one on the Sun's plate and the other on the Moon's. No sooner had the dog and cat drawn near the plates and begun to eat the food than they fell dead.

Then, pointing to the Sun and the Moon, the Five-times-fair One said to the King:

"These, my lord King, are your children. She gave them life whom you now keep walled up in the sewer."

On hearing this the King swooned, as did his mother also. When he had been revived, he asked her:

"What is this you tell me, O Five-times-fair One?"

"I have known all from the beginning," she answered. "Take their mother's bones from the sewer, that her children may kiss them."

The King called two of his henchmen and bade them open up the sewer and take the mother from within it. She was still alive.

She was dressed, and seated in a chair, and her children, the Sun and the Moon, were brought to her.

Then the Queen related how, when the children were born, she had seen a bright light in the house.

"Why did you not tell me of this?" asked the King.

"I feared your mother's evil works," she said.

Then the King ordered his mother's head to be struck off; and the King and the Queen lived on with their children.


## THE OLD MAN WHO CHEATED THE DEVIL

Once upon a time there was a fisherman who lived with his old wife. He cast his nets, but he caught few fish. One day he went where the water was deeper and threw out his nets. He caught no fish, but there was something heavy in the nets.

"What is this in my nets?" he said. He hauled them in, and what should

15ˑ

he see but a bottle with a stopper in it! He took hold of it and looked at it all over, but he could not make out what was inside that made it as heavy as iron.

"I'll open it, and we shall see what we shall see," he said.

He pulled out the stopper, and suddenly there was smoke, noise, and darkness.

The old man was frightened.

Suddenly, a horned devil appeared in the prow of his boat, who said to him:

"Old man, tell me what death you wish to die. I am such-and-such a devil, and I was bottled up by Solomon, who threw me into the sea a hundred and fifty fathoms deep. I swore that whoever should set me free ere forty years had passed, him would I make a King; but whoever should set me free after forty years had passed should die."

Said the old man to the devil: "But I did you a favour by freeing you."

Said the devil: "I have sworn it in the name of Solomon, and you must die."

"Hold hard!" said the old man. "I wonder greatly how you could ever have got into that bottle."

"Would you like to see for yourself how I got in?" asked the devil.

"That I would!" said the old man.

"Wait and you shall," said the devil. And suddenly he loosed a clap of thunder, and then he said from inside the bottle: "I am in."

The old man seized the stopper at once and thrust it into the bottle. Then he said:

"Now I shall throw you into the sea a hundred and fifty fathoms deep, never to come out again."

Said the devil: "Alas, I am undone!" And he begged the old man to let him out, and promised to make him a King.

"You shall never come out," said the old man, "unless you swear in the name of your great Solomon, and then I might set you free."

The devil, who could do nothing else, said:

"I swear in the name of Solomon that I will do you no harm, and I will show you the place where you may catch great numbers of fish every day."

The old man took out the stopper, and the devil again loosed a clap of thunder and a streak of lightning, and came out. Then he showed him the place where he might cast his nets and get a boatload of fish.

So the old man went and hauled in a great catch and took it home and lived right well.

## DAME CAT: OR THE WEDDING PATRON

Once upon a time there lived a King and a Queen who had three sons. Now it came to pass that the Queen fell ill; the doctors came and went about her, but none could discover the nature of her illness. So, after a while, she died. But after her death, the King lost his wealth, so that he, too, fell grievously sick, and at last he called his three sons to him and said:

"My children, I know that I am about to die, and I have summoned you to tell you this: as you know, we are not the rich folk that we once were. Our wealth has gone, our kingdom's wealth has gone, and I have nothing to leave you but this golden strap and our cat.

Which will you have, my son?" he asked the first, "the golden strap and my curse, or the cat and my blessing?"

The first son answered: "The golden strap, my father, and your curse."

The King put the same choice to the second son, who also said: "The golden strap and your curse."

The King called the third son and put the choice to him.

The third son answered: "The cat, my father, and your blessing."

He then bent and did obeisance to his father, kissed his hand, and received his blessing. Thereupon the priest was summoned to say the last rites over the King, who then departed this life. He was given a funeral and buried within three days.

The two elder sons took the strap and went away. They sold it, spent the money wantonly right and left, and came to a bad end. Let us leave them to their fate and come to the third and youngest son.

Every day the cat ran here and there, stealing bread, cheese, fish; she went out hunting rabbits and birds, and brought all back to the King's son. They fared very well. It was a case of "He who has his parents' blessing may climb mountains." But one day, when a year had gone by, Dame Cat brought the King's son a great quantity of food, so that he asked her:

"Why have you brought so much? Who will eat all this?"

Then she said to him:

"I have brought you so much because I am going away, and it will be two or three days before I return."

He was sad to hear that the cat was going away, for he did not know how to fend for himself. But the cat left him and, as she went on her way, she met a flock of partridges.

"Good day, Dame Cat," they said, "Whither away?"

197

"The Prince is to wed, my dears, and I have been asked to the wedding. If you, too, would like to see it, then follow me."

The birds followed her. Farther on, she met a troop of rabbits.

"Oh, good day, Dame Cat, and where are you going with your flock of partridges?"

"The Prince is to wed, my dears, and I have been asked to the wedding. I am taking the partridges with me. You may follow us if you like."

The rabbits followed on. Farther along the way, the cat met a flock of pigeons, who said:

"Good day, Dame Cat, and where are you going with your partridges and rabbits?"

"The Prince is to wed, my dears, and I have been asked to the wedding. You may follow me if you like."

All followed on behind. The cat went to the palace and knocked on the door. Rat-tat! The porter came out and said to her:

"Why come you to knock on our door?"

"My master, Prince So-and-So, has sent me with a message for the King."

The King at once ordered the doors to be opened, and the cat went in with the rabbits, partridges, and pigeons, and said to the King:

"My lord King, the Prince, my master, sends you his greetings and these partridges, rabbits, and pigeons for a tit-bit."

So the cat was bidden to come up into the palace. A table was laid, the meal was served, and she was invited to sit down and eat. When they had eaten their fill, she said to the King:

"The Prince sent me, my lord King, to ask for your daughter's hand in marriage."

When he heard this, the King was right glad, and said he would be honoured to have the Prince for his son-in-law.

"Then let us, my lord King, agree as to when the wedding shall be," said Dame Cat.

So they agreed, and next day, Dame Cat departed. She walked and walked till she reached home. She went in, and what should she see but the Prince, weeping and wailing because she had left him alone!

"You have no cause to weep," she said, "when I have made a compact for you to marry the King's daughter."

But he flew into a rage and said: "Why did you make such a compact?"

The cat told him not to bother his head about that, and to be sure that she would put matters right.

So they set out. They walked and walked till they came to a ravine.

were eager that he should have so lovely a wife. But how were they to get her? One day, one of the counsellors had an idea. He said to the King:

"O King, you know how capable and resourceful a man is our head-falconer. Nothing seems impossible to him. Why not send him to bring you the daughter of the King of China?"

So once more the King summoned the head-falconer, and said to him:

"I will give you forty days in which to bring me the Chinese King's daughter. Otherwise, your head will be cut off."

What could the poor man do but take to the road once again? After going a long way, not knowing what course to take, he came to a mill. A man was sitting close to the part where the flour was being poured in, and he kept licking and eating up all the flour coming out of the mill.

"What skill! What talent!" cried the head-falconer; but the flour-eater answered:

"I could not be more skilful than the famous head-falconer."

"I am the head-falconer," said he. "Will you come with me?"

The flour-eater gladly agreed to go with him, and the two set off together on their way. Presently they stumbled upon a man who had his ear to the ground and was listening intently. The head-falconer asked him what he was doing, and the man answered:

"I listen with my ear to the ground, and I can hear all the noise and voices round the earth, and so I know all that goes on in the world."

"What skill! What talent!" said the head-falconer, admiringly. But the ground-listener answered:

"My skill is nothing compared to that of the head-falconer."

"I am the head-falconer," said he. "Would you like to join company with us?"

The ground-listener was delighted to join company with the two comrades, and so they started off on their way again. As the three friends continued their journey, they chanced upon a man who was engaged in a most extraordinary work. He seized mountain-like rocks in one hand, and threw them at the mountains, which broke into pieces and were knocked down. The head-falconer exclaimed:

"What skill! What talent!" But the mountain-smasher answered:

"I could not possibly be like the head-falconer for skill."

"I am the head-falconer," said he. "We are on our way to fetch the Chinese King's daughter. Would you like to join us?"

The mountain-smasher consented and joined the company. As the four men travelled together, they encountered another man, and asked him who he was, whence he came, and where he was going.

16·

211

"They call me space-treader," he answered. "I left the town of A. a few minutes ago, and now I go to town S."

"What skill! What talent!" cried the head-falconer. But the space-treader answered:

"Oh, no! My skill it nothing compared with that of the head-falconer."

"I am the head-falconer," said he, "and we are going to fetch the Chinese King's daughter. Will you come with us?"

Thus the space-treader also joined the company. He folded the four companions in his arms, and in an instant, they were right before the palace of the Chinese King. There they sat on a big flat marble, just opposite the great gate.

The palace officers saw these strange men and informed the King of their arrival. The King sent for them immediately, and asked them who they were and from whence they came. The head-falconer told his story, and then he said:

"We have come to ask you for your daughter's hand on behalf of our King, who has commissioned us to take her to him."

"I have one condition to make," said the King of China. "I will give my daughter in marriage to your King if you can eat at one sitting all the food and bread that I appoint for you; and that is forty mule-loads of bread and forty cauldronfuls of cooked food."

The head-falconer looked troubled, but the flour-eater said:

"Don't you worry, my friend. Forty mule-loads of bread and forty cauldronfuls of food is hardly enough to satisfy me."

So when the agreed amount of bread and food was brought, the flour-eater gulped it all down in forty mouthfuls.

When the King of China saw what had happened, he said:

"I have another proposal to make. My daughter will accompany you to the fountain on the top of the Kaf Mountain. If you can bring some of that water to me ahead of my daughter, then I will consent to her marriage."

The King's daughter took her pitchers and went in flying haste to the fountain; but the space-treader was back with the water before she even arrived there.

The King was both amazed and angry, and he exclaimed:

"No, no! This will not do! What are you? Magicians or what? You do impossible things! I don't want you! Begone!"

The head-falconer was greatly troubled at being driven out in this manner. But the mountain-smasher said to him:

"You don't need to worry, comrade. Wait till evening, and when the people retire, I shall shoulder the palace and carry it off with the Chinese King and his daughter."

True enough, when evening came, the ground-listener put his ear to the ground and listened. All was quiet in the King's palace. Everone was asleep. So the mountain-smasher shouldered the palace and started off on his journey. When the travellers grew tired and wanted a rest, they set the palace down on a plain, and then lighted a fire to warm themselves. The Chinese King woke from his sleep and looked through the window. What place was this? Where were they? Then, noticing the men, he called to the head-falconer and said:

"For goodness sake, take my daughter away. I am willing to give you as much gold as you like, if you will only take my palace back to its proper place before daybreak."

The head-falconer consented, and the palace was taken back to its proper place. Then they took the Chinese King's daughter back to their own King, who was greatly pleased, and ordered his treasury officers to pay the head-falconer three thousand pieces of gold. Again the officers intended to pay him only three thousand piastres. But the King's daughter felt in her heart that the officers were wrongdoers, so she sent for the head-falconer, and then asked the King to enquire how much money he had received. The King asked the man how much he had been paid. He replied that he had received a thousand piastres when he brought the falcon, two thousand when he brought the bird-bones, and now three thousand piastres. The King's daughter was furious, and she said:

"What an indifferent King and an unjust sovereign you are!" and she had the King beheaded.

Then the head-falconer was brought to the throne. There was great merriment which lasted forty days and forty nights, at the end of which the new King married the daughter of the King of China, and they were happy for ever after.

## STORIES FROM NASREDDIN HODJA

One day the Hodja needed a cauldron for laundry purposes, so he borrowed one from a neighbour. Next day, he returned the cauldron to its owner, placing a small pot in it. As the neighbour took the cauldron, he noticed the small pot inside, and asked:

"What is this thing here, Hodja?"

"Didn't you know that your cauldron was pregnant?" answered the Hodja. "This baby cauldron was born last night."

The neighbour saw no objection to this, and carried both cauldron and pot away.

Some days passed; then once again, the Hodja needed to borrow the cauldron. His neighbour was glad enough to let him have it. This time, however, the Hodja, who was usually very particular in returning borrowed objects promptly, seemed to have forgotten the cauldron. So one day the neighbour came and asked him if he could let him have his cauldron back. The Hodja shook his head sadly.

"Dear neighbour," he said, "I am very sorry, but your cauldron is dead."

The man stared in utter astonishment and said:

"What on earth do you mean, Hodja? How can a cauldron die?"

The Hodja answered in equal surprise:

"What a queer person you must be! When the cauldron gave birth to a child, you were glad enough to believe it; but when the poor thing dies, you will not believe that! Well, well!"


One day a neighbour came to the Hodja who was standing outside the door, and said:

"Hodja, I have to go to the mill. Will you please let me have your donkey?"

The Hodja did not like the idea, so he said: "The donkey is not here." But at that very moment, the donkey started to bray in the stable. The neighbour was very surprised, and exclaimed:

"Oh, Hodja! You said the donkey was not there; but you can hear him braying, as though to make himself known. I am surprised at you!"

"What a strange fellow you are!" answered the Hodja, shaking his head indignantly. "You don't believe what I, a white-beard, say, and yet you will believe what a donkey says!"


The Hodja was taken ill, so seriously that he thought he was going to die. So he said to his wife:

"Come here, my dear. Will you please go and put on your best dress, and adorn yourself as finely as you can? Wear all your ornaments. I want to see you look as beautiful as the moon. Then come and sit near me."

214

"Oh, my dear Hodja," answered his wife, "of course I'll do whatever you say, but ... Wouldn't it be a strange thing to do now? Wouldn't it be rather unbecoming for me to deck myself out while you are so very ill? I am afraid I can't bring myself to do it! No, no! Not for the whole world would I do such a thing! What on earth made you think of so queer a thing?"

The Hodja insisted, saying very seriously:

"Do just as I tell you, my dear. I want you to look like a fresh flower."

Then his wife grew impatient, and said in a rebellious tone:

"No, no, no! I can't do it! I won't do it! It would be like making fun of your illness. Please spare me, and stop urging me to such strange actions."

The Hodja gave a deep sigh, and then he explained.

"Listen, my dear," he said. "You do not understand what I mean. You don't really see things as I do. You see, I feel that I am living through the last hours of my life. Azrail[1] keeps going round my bed, and he intends to carry my soul away. But I thought that if you adorned yourself and looked very beautiful, he might change his mind, and prefer to have you instead."

The Hodja went to the market-place on business. All of a sudden, a man came running up to him and said, excitedly:

"Oh, Hodja, Hodja! Hurry! Come on! Your house is on fire! I knocked at the door repeatedly, but no one answered, so I came running to find you. Come quickly and put the fire out!"

The Hodja was quite undisturbed, and answered calmly:

"Don't you worry, my son. In our house we apply the rule of division of labour. My wife takes care of home affairs, and so, as the fire is in the house, it is her job to deal with it. She must be out visiting a neighbour. Will you please go and find her, and tell her the house is on fire?"

So saying, the Hodja went on with his work.

It was a fine summer day, and the Hodja was on his way to the vine-yard, merrily driving his donkey before him. He came to a standstill when he saw two boys fighting fiercely, pulling at a crow, and getting at each other's throats. In a second, he was between the fighters, holding them both fast.

---

1. The Angel of Death.

"What is the matter, lads?" he cried. "Aren't you ashamed to fight thus? You will kill the bird between you. Let the poor thing go, let go!"

The boys were glad to see the Hodja, and one of them said:

"A good thing you came along, Hodja! For goodness sake, judge between us. This bird was on top of that tree. I made my chum stand on my shoulders so that he could climb into the tree, and in that way he caught the crow. Now he says the bird is his, and that I have no claim to it. But if he had not stood on my shoulders, he could not have been able to get up into the tree to catch it."

"Oh, indeed!" shouted the other. "So you think I would not have been able to climb the tree but for your old shoulders, eh? I would have climbed it without you and in spite of you. You asked me to stand on you shoulders, and I did so just to please you. Besides, catching a bird is not easy. It's not like picking fruit. A bird is a living thing and has wings. If you don't know how to go at it rightly, whiz! Off it flies into the air, and you are left behind just staring! It needs quite skill to catch a bird. And you, poor thing, are not even capable of catching a frog on the ground. It was I who caught this bird. And it is mine, my very own!"

The Hodja, having listened to both parties, said:

"Gently, boys, gently! Now listen to me. First of all, give me the poor bird, and stop pulling and pushing between you. Then hear my judgement. This bird belongs to neither of you singly. It belongs to you both. If crow's flesh were edible, I would cut it in two and divide it between you, but the crow is not an edible bird. You had better take this money and buy candy with it."

The Hodja took the bird and gave the boys some coins to buy candy. As they ran happily away, he let the bird free. But the poor crow, after the rough treatment it had suffered from the boys, could not fly very far. It flew only a little way, and then alighted on the back of a water buffalo which was grazing in the fields. The Hodja was delighted to see this, and hurried to the place where the buffalo was grazing.

"Oh, my brave hawk!" he cried to the crow. "What splendid game you have caught for me!" and he drove the buffalo before him to his house.

Soon afterwards, the owner of the water buffalo came to the field, and not finding the beast, went in search of him. Finally, some one told him that the Hodja had taken the animal away. The peasant came to the Hodja's house, and knocked furiously at the door. The Hodja looked out of the window and saw the man standing at the door below.

216

"Who are you?" he demanded. "And what do you want?"

"I am the buffalo's owner," answered the man, angrily, "and I have come to take it away. I ask you, what right had you to take a water buffalo grazing in the fields and bring it here? I have been searching for it this long time, in anxiety and difficulty, and now I am very tired. See how sore and swollen my feet are!"

The Hodja was angry too, and he retorted:

"Look here, my man! Do you think you're on a mountain-top and can shout yourself hoarse, or what? You are in a town, and there is a law-court in this place to which you can appeal. To hunt is lawful, and the quarry belongs to the one who catches it. I bought a crow from two boys, and paid for it; then I sent it forth, and it caught the buffalo as game. Now you come here and claim ownership of the buffalo! I won't have it, I tell you! I won't have it! Nor will I let you have the water buffalo. Be off with you!"

The peasant departed, and went straight to the law-court to make his complaint to the judge. The judge sent for the Hodja, who told him the whole story in detail, and hinted that he would send the judge a potful of water buffalo butter as a present. The judge pondered the matter for a while; then he shook his head and pronounced judgement.

"The game caught by a bird bought with money is lawful," he said, "even though that bird may be a crow. Therefore, the water buffalo is the property of the Hodja."

Next day, the Hodja sent the judge the promised butter in an earthenware pot. The judge was very pleased with the butter, and used it for his morning breakfast. But on the fourth morning, he noticed some strange foul matter underneath. He could hardly believe his eyes, and dipped the spoon further into the pot. Yes, sure enough, the remaining substance was not butter, but buffalo's excrement.

He sent for the Hodja immediately. When the Hodja arrived, the judge roared at him:

"How dare you do this to me, the judge of the town! How dare you! A blunder, a great blunder, has been committed!"

"O judge!" came the calm and quiet answer, "You committed the blunder yourself three days ago!"

The Hodja took his place in the pulpit one day, and was ready to preach.

"Oh, people!" he began, "Do you know what I am going to preach to you about?"

"No, we do not!" was the unanimous reply.

"Well, then," said the Hodja, "since you do not know, why should I tell you?"

And he descended from the pulpit and went away.

Next day, he mounted the pulpit again and said:

"Oh, people! Do you know what I am going to talk to you about?"

This time, everybody answered: "Yes, we know!"

"Well, then," replied the Hodja, "since you know it already, there is no need for me to tell you."

And once again he left the pulpit and went away.

On the next day, the congregation discussed the matter, and they decided that, if the Hodja asked the same question again, some should say "Yes", and others should say "No".

The Hodja did ask the same question again from the pulpit, and the people answered: "Some of us know and some do not!"

"Fine!" replied the Hodja. "Let those who know tell those who do not know!"

And leaving the pulpit once more, he walked out.

# NOTES

ATT + Arabic numerals refer to type-number in *A. Aarne & S. Thompson:* The Types of the Folk-Tale, Second Revision. *FF Communications* 184, Helsinki 1961.

THE SOLDIER AND THE BAD MAN (p. 1). ATT 361. Finland. Manuscript: Suomalaisen Kirjallisuuden Seuran, Helsinki, B. A. Paldani 2. Collected 1852 by B. A. Paldani. Told at Karvia.

PIGSKIN (p. 10). ATT 314. Finland. Manuscript: Suomalaisen Kirjallisuuden Seuran, Helsinki, T. E. Rauvola 9. Collected 1890 by T. E. Rauvola. Told at Pori.

THE PRINCESS AND THE PEASANT (p. 17). ATT 530. Finland. Manuscript: Suomalaisen Kirjallisuuden Seuran, Helsinki, M. Nurmio 9 – M. Jaaksi 25y. Collected 1887 by M. Nurmio. Told by M. Jaaksi at Laihia.

THE RAT (p. 23). ATT 402. Sweden. Manuscript: Västsvenska Folkminnesarkivet, Gothenburg, "The Liungman Collection" Acc. No. 461. Collected 1926 by C. B. Johansson. Told by his father J. E. Johansson at Åsbo, Västergötland.

THE INHERITANCE (p. 26). ATT 1650+1652+1653+1045+1073+1072+1071. Finland [Swedish]. Manuscript: V. L. Cajander. Collected s. a. by V. L. Cajander. Told by an unknown informant at Lappträsk, Österbotten. Printed in *Nyland* 6 (Helsingfors 1896) 28.

THE SILLY BOY (p. 28). ATT 1696+1685. Sweden. Manuscript: Folkminnesarkivet, Nordiska Museet, Stockholm, Hammarstedtska Arkivet: Sagor. Collected 1880 by R. Bergström. Told by an unknown informant.

THE GIANT'S TREASURE (p. 33). ATT 328+1121. Sweden. Manuscript: Västsvenska Folkminnesarkivet, Gothenburg, "The Liungman Collection" Acc. No. 503. Collected 1926 by A.-L. Wallin. Told by her mother Carolina Wallin at Gunnilbo, Västmanland.

SALENTO AND SØLENTO (p. 37). ATT 870. Norway. Manuscript: Norsk Folkeminnesamling, Oslo, NFS H. H. Nordbø I,170. Collected 1879 by H. H. Nordbø. Told by Gonil Hegna at Bø, Telemark Fylke.

THE ANIMAL SONS-IN-LAW (p. 41). ATT 552B. Norway. Manuscript: Norsk Folkeminnesamling, Oslo, NFS Knut Strompdal VII,26. Collected 1926/27 by K. Strompdal. Told by Simon Toft at Nordsømna, Nordland Fylke. Printed in *K. Strompdal,* Gamalt frå Helgeland II (*Norsk Folkeminnelags Skrifter* 40, Oslo 1938) 35.

STRONG PETER AND HIS MEN (p. 43). ATT 301B*. Norway [Lappish]. Manuscript: Norsk Folkeminnesamling, Oslo. Collected 1921 by J. Qvigstad. Told by Nils Stubbeng at Lyngen, Troms Fylke. Printed in *J. Qvigstad,* Lappiske eventyr og sagn III (Oslo 1929) 82.

BUTTER BALL SPA (p. 47). ATT 327C. Norway. Manuscript: Norsk Folkeminnesamling, Oslo. Collected 1916 by Edvard Langset. Told by Elen Kristensdotter Flatsetøy and her mother Karen Anderson Flatsetøy at Frei, Møre and Romsdal Fylke.

THE STORY OF PRINCE HLINI (p. 50). ATT 317A*. Iceland. Manuscript: Handritasafn Landsbókasafns Íslands, Reykjavík 416,165. Collected s. a. by Jón Árnason. Told by Ebenezer Matthíasson at Flatey, Barðarstrandar sýsla. Printed in *J. Árnason, Íslenzkar Þjóðsögur og Æfintýri* II (Leipzig 1864) 431; ³II (Reykjavík 1956) 412.

WAKE-WELL AND HIS BROTHERS (p. 53). ATT 653. Iceland. Collected s. a. by Magnús Grímsson. Told by a farmer at Biskuptungur, Árnessýsla. Printed in *J. Árnason, Íslenzkar Þjóðsögur og Æfintýri* II (Leipzig 1864) 471; ³II (Reykjavík 1956) 447.

THE STORY OF HILD THE GOOD STEPMOTHER (p. 56). ATT 934E**. Iceland. Manuscript: Handritasafn Landsbókasafns Íslands, Reykjavík 533,495. Collected s. a. by Jón Árnason. Told by Kristína Jónsdóttir in Reykjavík. Printed in *J. Árnason, Íslenzkar Þjóðsögur og Æfintýri* II (Leipzig 1864) 391; ³II (Reykjavík 1956) 375.

KING WIVERN (p. 64). ATT 433B. Denmark. Manuscript: Dansk Folkemindesamling, Copenhagen, DFS XI,116–120. Collected 1854 by Niels Levinsen. Told by Maren Mathisdatter at Furreby, Northern Jutland. Printed in *N. Levinsen,* Folkeeventyr fra Vendsyssel (Copenhagen 1958) 26, and in *L. Bødker,* Danske Folkeeventyr (Copenhagen 1960) 74.

ANN GEJ AND VISIVEJ (p. 70). ATT 313C. Denmark. Manuscript: Dansk Folkemindesamling, Copenhagen, DFS IV,333–38. Collected 1856 by Nicolaj Christensen. Told by Lars Østtrup at Vester Vedsted, Northern Jutland.

IN THE HILLMAN'S SERVICE (p. 78). ATT 1000+1003+1004+1002+1012+1006+1005+1008+1010+1115+1153. Denmark, Manuscript unknown. Collected 1887 by Kr. Nielsen at Ringgive, Eastern Jutland. Printed in *Skattegraveren IX* (Kolding 1887) 5, and in *L. Bødker,* Danske Folkeeventyr (Copenhagen 1960) 17.

HOW A SMITH MADE HIS FORTUNE (p. 87). ATT 935. Germany. Manuscript: Archiv für Volkskunde, Marburg, Sammlung Henssen, W.H. Nr. 1495. Collected 1937 by G. Henssen. Told by Gerhard Nehus at Rütenbrock, Emsland.

THE PRINCESS IN THE UNDERWORLD (p. 90). ATT 301. Germany. Manuscript: Archiv für Volkskunde, Marburg, ZA Nr. 32659, Sammlung Henssen W. Nr. 858. Collected 1931 by G. Henssen. Told by Gertrudis Gerwert at Gross-Reken, Münsterland.

ONCE IN, NEVER OUT AGAIN (p. 92). ATT 303. Austria. Manuscript: Archiv für Volkskunde, Marburg. Collected 1936/37 by Anton Dolleschall. Told by Kurt Seidl at St. Blasen, Steiermark.

MICHEL MICHELKLEINER'S GOOD LUCK (p. 98). ATT 1875+1653. Luxemburg. Collected 1960 by Joseph Hess. Told by Johann Wiltgen at Moutfort.

MASTER SLY (p. 99). ATT 1535. Luxemburg. Printed in *N. Gredt,* Sagenschatz des Luxemburger Landes (Luxemburg 1883) 478.

WITHOUT WORRY (p. 103). ATT 922. Holland. Manuscript: Centraal Bureau voor Nederlandsche Volkskunde van de Nederlandsche Akademie van Wetenschappen, Amsterdam, Boekenoogen. Collected 1901 by C. Bakker. Told by Dirk Schuurman, Broek at Waterland, Noord-Holland.

THE THREE PEDLARS (p. 104). ATT 613. Collected 1909 by G. J. Klokman. Told at Laag-Keppel, Gelderland. Printed in *Driemaandelijksche Bladen* IX, 7; *G. J. Klokman,* Hendrik Eume (Baarn 1936) 72; *J. R. W. Sinninghe,* Vijftig Nederlandsche Sprookjes (Amsterdam 1942) 31.

THE WONDER CHILD (p. 108). ATT 652. Holland. Manuscript: Provinciaal Genootschap van Kunsten en Wetenschappen van Noord-Brabant, 's Hertogenbosch, Aug. Sassen. Collected about 1890 by Aug. Sassen. Told by an old woman at Helmond, Noord-Brabrant. Printed in *J. R. W. Sinninghe,* Vijftig Nederlandsche Sprookjes (Amsterdam 1942) 37.

CHRIST AND PETER (p. 112) ATT 822+791+752A. Holland. Collected 1956 by J. R. W. Sinninghe. Told by Janus Peys at Etten, Noord-Brabant.

THE SMALL-TOOTH DOG (p. 114). ATT 425X. England. Collected between 1890 and 1895 by Sidney Oldhall Addy. Told by unknown informant from Norton in Derbyshire. Printed in *S. O. Addy,* Household Tales (London & Sheffield 1895) 1.

KING ARTHUR AND THE DRAGON (p. 116). ATT÷. England. Collected by Ruth Tongue. Local traditions of Carhampton and Billbrook, Somerset.

KING ARTHUR AND THE WHITE HORSE (p. 117). ATT÷. England. Collected 1931 by Christina Hole. Told by unknown informant from Frodsham, Cheshire.

THE TIDDY MUN (p. 118). ATT÷. England. Collected 1891 by M. C. Balfour. Told by a little girl in Lincolnshire. Printed in *Folk-Lore* II (1891) 149.

THE GWRAIG AND THE THREE BLOWS (p. 120). ATT 400*. Wales. Collected 1880 by Wirt Sykes. Told by unknown informant. Printed in *British Goblins.*

THE KING OF THE BLACK ART (p. 122). ATT 325. Scotland. Manuscript: Sound archive of School of Scottish Studies RL 1459,A7. Collected 1956 by Hamish Henderson. Told by John Stewart, Glasgow.

FARQUHAR SON OF ALASDAIR (p. 131). ATT÷. Scotland. Manuscript: Archive of School of Scottish Studies, D. J. MacDonald. Written down by the informant, D. J. MacDonald, 1956. Printed in *Gairm* 15, Spring 1956.

CLUASACH AND THE SEA-WOMAN (p. 135). ATT 1889H + 1179*. Ireland. Manuscript in private possession (Séamus O'Duilearga). Collected 1925 by Séamus O'Duilearga. Told by Séan O'Conaill at Cilrialaig, Baile'n Sgéilg, Co. Kerry. Printed in *Séamus O'Duilearga,* Leabhar Sheáin Í Chonaill (Dublin 1948) 259.

THE WOMAN WHO WENT TO HELL (p. 136). ATT 425J. Ireland. Manuscript: Irish Folklore Commission, Dublin, Ms. Vol. 242,75. Collected 1936 by Seosamh O'Dálaigh. Told by Tadhg O'Guithín at Dunquin, Co. Kerry. Printed in *S. O'Suilleabháin,* Scéalta Cráibhtheacha (Dublin 1952) 141.

THE SON OF THE KING OF THE SPECKLED MOUNTAIN (p. 142). ATT÷.
Ireland. Manuscript in private possession (Séamus O'Duilearga). Collected 1932 by
S. O'Duilearga. Told by Mícheál Breathnach at Mám, Co. Galway. Printed in *Béaloideas* 6 (Dublin 1936) 298.

JACQUES (p. 155). ATT 307. Belgium. Manuscript: R. Pinon, Liège. Collected 1893
by G. Gilles. Told by unknown informant at Vottem.

THE OLD COBBLER (p. 156). ATT 1640. Belgium. Manuscript: R. Pinon, Liège.
Collected 1891 by A. Colson. Told by Marie Josèphe Marck at Vottem.

BLUE-BEARD (p. 158). ATT 312. France. Manuscript: Musée national des arts et
traditions populaires, Paris, No. 45.271, Ariane de Félice: Enquête sur quelques
traditions orales recueillies dans la region de Monsireigne, Vendée.

MARION AND JEANNE (p. 160). ATT 480+510A+1180. France. Manuscript:
Bibliothèque de l'Institut Catholique, Paris, Manuscrits Victor Smith I, 504–28.
Collected between 1870 and 1875 by Jean-Baptiste Victor Smith. Told by Nannette
Lévesque at Fraisse by Firminy (Loire).

THE BELL ROCK (p. 166). ATT÷. Portugal. Printed in *Manuel Vieira Dinis,*
Lendas da Citânia de Sanfins, *Douro-Litoral* (boletim), s. V, IX, p. 66.

THE DRAWSTRING BAG (p. 167). ATT÷. Portugal. Printed in *Rebelo Bonito,*
Um conto tradicional português – A Rolinha, *Douro-Litoral* (boletim), s. VII, IX,
p. 969.

THE MERCHANT AND HIS THREE DAUGHTERS (p. 173). ATT 311. Spain.
Printed in *Joan Amades,* Les cent millors rondalles populars (Barcelona 1953) 93.

THE DRAGON (p. 174). ATT 300. Spain. Printed in *Maria de Azkue,* Euskaleriaren
Yakintza (Madrid 1942) 131.

THE BLACK BRIDE AND THE WHITE BRIDE (p. 176). ATT 403. Italy. Manuscript: Museo Nazionale delle Arti e delle Tradizioni Popolari, Roma.

THE THREE ORANGES (p. 178). ATT 408. Italy. Printed in *Ranieri Mario Cossar,*
Storia dai tre nerànz, *Soc. Filologica Friulana* (Udine 1930) 82.

THE SERPENT SON (p. 182). ATT 425F + 621. Italy. Printed in *Letterio di
Francia,* Fiabe e novelle calabresi (Torino 1929 = *Pallante* 8: 3/4) 37.

THE VILE MOTHER-IN-LAW (p. 189). ATT 707. Greece. Manuscript: Folklore
Archives, Athens, No. 2279,431. Collected 1958 by G. K. Spyridakis. Told by Maria
Issechos in the island Leros of the Dodecanese.

THE OLD MAN WHO CHEATED THE DEVIL (p. 195). ATT 331. Greece.
Manuscript: Folklore Archives, Athens, No. 2279,434. Collected 1958 by G. K. Spyridakis. Told by John Issechos in the island Leros of the Dodecanese.

DAME CAT: OR THE WEDDING PATRON (p. 197). ATT 545B. Greece. Collected 1952 by Pan. Kritikos. Told by Maria Kritikou in the island Patmos of the
Dodecanese. Printed in *Laographia* 15 (1953–54) 328.

MASTER TRUTHFUL (p. 201). ATT 889. Greece. Manuscript: Folklore Archives,
Athens, No. 2304,97. Collected 1959 by G. K. Spyridakis. Told by Emman Psathas
in the island of Milos.

THE POOR MAN WHO SOLD HIS SOUL TO THE DEVIL (p. 203). ATT 810. Greece. Collected 1938 by John Eleutherakis. Told in the village Roússa Eklissiá, Crete. Printed in *Myson* 7 (1939) 157.

THE GIRL OUT OF WHOSE MOUTH CAME A SNAKE (p. 205). ATT 507B +945+cf. ATT 1169. Turkey. Manuscript in private possession (Ahmet Kudsi Tecer). Collected 1942 by Özcan San. Told by Fatma in the village of Gümüshane in Anatolia.

THE HEAD-FALCONER (p. 209). ATT 513A. Turkey. Manuscript in private possession (Ahmet Kudsi Tecer). Collected 1959 by Veli Ak. Told by Ahmet Öztürk in the village of Kapakli in Anatolia.

STORIES FROM NASREDDIN HODJA (p. 213). ATT 1592B+cf. 1354+ATT÷. Turkey. From various sources.